The Native Horses
of Scotland

ISBN 0 85976 190 8

Exclusive distribution in the United States
of America and Canada by Humanities Press
Inc., Atlantic Highlands, NJ 07716, USA.

Phototypeset by Print Origination, Formby, Liverpool.
Printed in Great Britain by Bell & Bain Ltd, Glasgow.

The Native Horses of Scotland

Scottish Breeds of Horses and their Folk

ANDREW F. FRASER

JOHN DONALD PUBLISHERS LTD
EDINBURGH

Acknowledgements

I am grateful to many people and several institutions for help with research on the subject matter and in the preparation of the manuscript. Special debts of gratitude are owed to the following:

For illustrative material and information Professors C. Fraser, J. Giffroy, W. Howell, M. Vandeplassche, Y. LeGal, C. Barker, R. Orr and B. Payton; Mr. W. Taylor, Mr. and Mrs. D. Charles, Mr. E. Ryan; the unit of Medical Audio Visual Services of Memorial University; the Archives of Scotland, Nova Scotia, Ontario and Saskatchewan; the Highland Pony Society, the Clydesdale Horse Societies in Scotland and Canada.

As reference sources, the following books were of special value: *The Ballad and the Plough*, by David Kerr Cameron; *Pit Pony Heroes*, by Eric Squires; *The Domesticated Animals*, by David Low; *Clydesdale*, by A. MacCallum Scott; *The Horse*, by W. Youatt; *The Clydesdale Horse*, by E. Baird; *The Book of Livestock*, by W. Toole; *Mayhew's Illustrated Horse Doctor* and *Mayhew's Illustrated Horse Management*; *Highland Ponies with Reminiscences of Highland Men*, by John McDonald; *History of the Highlands and the Highland Clans*, by James Browne.

In the production of the manuscript, some material was taken from *Days of the Garron*, by the author. The word processing was done by Miss D. Caines.Some portions were reviewed by Mrs. J. Fairley. Artwork was done by Mr. C. George. Finally, acknowledgement is made for diligent research carried out by Miss N. Aitchison, to whose memory the book is humbly dedicated.

Andrew Ferguson Fraser

Contents

Introduction

A bright blue heaven, heat of that August afternoon, far sounds of water moving against the Scottish coast and down a hillside had all produced a rare tranquillity of soul in me. I moved among patches of heather, bracken and gorse, making my way from a distant track of stony road to a green slope which faced towards the ocean and the sun, seeking a resting place. Protected from the sources of crass life by mountains and sea, one might somehow slip the alien world. Escape to the past might still be possible, if only for a while and only in thought. On an even surface of close-grazed turf I stretched out to observe the stillness of time and nature in that place of beauty and surrender my thoughts to chance; soon I drowsed lightly.

The new world in which I wakened was busy with bird calls, the movement of fine grass stems bowing in the lightly brushing breeze and the activity of insect life around the clumps of nearby gorse. Odours around had thickened into a heady mixture from small flowers and earlier traffic of sheep. But there was another dominating presence. Irregular heavy sounds, switching and cropping sounds, and wisps of an old familiar odour informed me that I was in an equine world. The sun was over the western ocean as I sat up, slowly taking in the scene; several 'working-class' horses grazed gradually in my direction. As they moved easily, cropping the sweet herbage and swishing their tails, it was evident that they also found their pleasure in this privileged lap of mother nature. One after the other they saw me sitting there, quite close, but posing no threat and inviting no great curiosity. Taking a slight change in direction upwards on the hillside, they grazed onwards out of view. This felt like some short scene from history, one which I should review in a play with the horse on centre stage, in times gone by, in the theatre of my homeland. This land—and the horses of its past with it—was worthy of the many lovers it would always have, in times better or worse.

A million individual horses were needed to maintain all of Scotland throughout the long periods of its social, agricultural and industrial revolution and evolution, a time when Scotland had hopes of power galore. The tail end of the work-horse era is still within living memory. It was really not so long ago, for some of us.

The Native Horses of Scotland

At the age of eight, three years before World War II, I saw my first Highland ponies running out on the hillside near Dunvegan, Skye, and was put on one to ride—a sturdy yellow gelding. The relationship was exciting but short-lived. Soon after, a fractured leg suffered in a fall from a dry-stone sheep pen required my removal to hospital in Glasgow. Four years later, living close to the blacksmith's smiddy, I got to know by sight every horse in the parish of Strath. When the travelling stallion arrived from the Department of Agriculture in May to take up summer residence and breed the mares of the parish, it was like a visit by Pegasus. A grey horse each year, he glimmered with grooming; mane, tail, forelock and feathers flew as he danced in his red striped surcingle, his walker by his head, striding out in a fresh direction each day. The arch of crested neck, the sharp pluck of each foot, the tail carriage, the impatient 'half-pass' gait, this was surely the ultimate in power, elegance and natural beauty. Would it be possible to work with the animal? Yes, I got to clean out his stall, and thus entered the service of the horse.

Throughout one long summer, in the midst of World War II, a Clydesdale mare called Polly was a working partner of mine in Midlothian. Our job was quite simply to shift about 200 tons of cow manure from the midden at the back of the farm dairy and spread it over a large area of grassland several miles away. The working conditions for both of us were excellent. Polly was young and strong, our cart was in good order and I was keen. We could eat well when the day's work was over. We got all the needed rest in our separate quiet quarters at night. We got enough time in the early morning to gather our wits, and harness ourselves in the operation. Sometimes, in the early days of this work, it seemed that it was without end; the midden seemed to be bottomless. Better it should never end, one thought, for the war news was not good and ours seemed the only peaceful enterprise in the whole world. It could be the end of a boyhood, and perhaps a horsehood, too, when the job would end and the partnership be broken.

With the rich odour of my trade immovable on me I was a singular failure in social ventures. In any event, the young women who went to the Saturday night dances in the nearby town were a different species. Their expressions, their gestures of shoulder or head made them much more difficult to comprehend than the mare. Though they smelled so richly of perfume, which was nice on first impact, this was not the honest smell of reality, of leather, sweat, manure or axle

2

grease. Their society appeared coy and not to want the intrusion of an apprentice carter, suffering agonies of confusion in the whole ritual charade. Anyhow coyness is really an equine trait which makes human coquetry seem poorly developed by comparison!

A queen among creatures was Polly thereafter. What body-brushing was needed for that sheen of dark coat. The long tangled strands of mane had all to be combed out. The bang of her short tail had to be kept clean and trim. The mare's velveteen face had to be smoothed more often and the chin of her lower lip could be teased till it puckered, impishly. Her legs, of course, needed much combing and brushing of the long sweep of white feathered hair down the back of her shanks. All the hair draping her hooves needed firm brushing to be kept clean and to flow easily with movement. Even the grimy soles of her feet got cleaned out better, out of extra fondness and respect. Yes, fond respect was what a horse could implant in a heart in the turmoil of emotions, in the hurting loneliness of youth.

Polly had her own pride, a lot of it in fact. Her pride was in her capacity for work. The fuller the load in her cart, the better she stepped out. The longer the working day stretched on, the harder she pulled. On the last journey of the day her empty cart became a chariot as she raced homewards at a clip with the bumping, bouncing cart. A zest for life can be learned from a good horse. The mare had each week-end off. She luxuriated in private idleness on Sunday; she knew the Sabbath as the day of rest but I did not. So, in restlessness, I would walk alone across field after field, over quiet country roads and through woods, only turning homewards as dusk descended. I was looking closely at mother nature, seeking some special message from all I saw. Slowly I got this message, quite simply it was a private hope for a distant future in which there would be meaning consistent with the natural order of living things. A great hope grew for a better understanding of the magic of nature. There were some smaller selfish hopes too and hope for a better being. Optimism was discovered as partial answer to the amorphous dissatisfaction with the endurances of youth. Now, when I occasionally travel streets and roads of Lothian, optimism is not far off; neither is Polly's ghost and the ghosts of all her tribe; equine heroes without a memorial. Perhaps this book will serve the purpose.

Today Scotland has three breeds of native horse: the Shetland Pony, the Highland Pony and the Clydesdale. Formerly there existed a

Galloway breed but this now is believed extinct. In addition, various breed types were recognised in certain locations, notably the Rhum Pony, the Skye Pony, the Mull Pony. The latter are still unofficially recognised collectively as the Western Isles Type of Highland Pony. A few specimens of the Eriskay Pony have been preserved and these are still given their ancient identity by some enthusiasts of the animal and by the Rare Breeds Survival Trust.

Of course Scotland had many other types of horses, not necessarily belonging to specific breeds. Some of these were of 'anonymous breeding' while others were deliberately produced by selected crossing of breeds. As a result there were horses simply called cart horses, vanners, hacks, drayhorses, coach horses and the like. Cavalry horses were either of large Highland Pony type for the Lovat Scouts or grey mounts selected for Scotland's only true cavalry—The Scots Greys. Another service horse was the humble pit pony, usually of the Shetland breed, but sometimes out of uncertain pony stock, of a stature suited to the mines where they spent their working lives.

The origin of Scotland's ponies is obscured in prehistory but the development of the world-famous Clydesdale can be traced fairly accurately. Although some points are controversial, such as the true nature of the 'Low-Country' breed which contributed to its foundation, and the personage to whom credit should be given for its formation, the Clydesdale's story is clear. Romantic tails of shipwrecked Spanish horses swimming to Scottish shores linger strongly in folklore. These seem to contain some truth. The Roman advance into the Scottish south may have left some military horses behind. Archaeologists have recognised a 'Celtic' pony in Scotland which is considered to have had a vaguely European origin. That Nordic strains of horse and pony reached Scotland by Norse invasion is another strongly held belief which fits many facts. For all that, Scotland's horses have been as much a part of the country as its mountains and glens, woods and streams. The Scottish horses and their people were intimately associated throughout times of fortune and misfortune. The association was honourable and essential to both the horse and to Scottish society. An account of this is overdue.

1. Some Lineage

A study of the complex web of joint human and animal history and prehistory helps to solve problems of origins. The close horse-and-man relationship has several advantages in this type of sociobiology. Horses and ponies might not, at first glance, seem to offer great assistance in studying historical sociology but they can provide many clues. They use potentially arable land to which mankind in also attached. The pony has been spread from its early homelands to every inhabited part of the world. Isolated communities of ponies even continue to exist very successfully in areas abandoned by man. In addition to being ubiquitous, horses are numerous; there may be 60 million around the world today. The equine biologist has a wealth of material with which to study the trail of the horse in history and in association with man. Adequate written records of history only began 200 years ago. Earliest writing, in any form, only goes back to 4000 B.C. Even that relates only to isolated populations in the Middle East. For many human societies, historical records of culture are comparatively recent. Any supportive evidence of prehistoric activities obtained from man's associated animals is very valuable circumstantial evidence of his early story.

The horse is senior to man as an established species. His life goes back ten million years, to man's two million. Pony history, both distant and recent, can be seen as an historical subject. The horse has had associations with mankind, perhaps from our beginnings. With the horse, man has had power to till land, to travel, to wage war and to symbolise economic and social trappings. The study of equine population is therefore rewarding, not only for what it reveals about its own adaptations, but also for what it suggests about any human population with which it is evidently associated.

The horse was well-established through many areas of the world long before mankind had succeeded in doing so. The varieties of early forms of the horse have been found in archaeological discoveries, particularly throughout Central and Northern Europe. Through these findings the evolution of the horse can be traced.

The early horse became vulnerable to a predator in the form of man.

The Native Horses of Scotland

Early cave man feasted on wild horses. The skeletal remains of about 100,000 horses have been discovered in a Cro-Magnon cave in France. Human intelligence eventually prevailed and man learned to put the horse to alternative, and better, use. Mounted on tame horses, he became a warrior of a new dimension. The wheel allowed the development of the war chariot, the first offensive military vehicle.

The Hittites from Asia Minor were the first people to make full use of the horse in warfare. This allowed them to acquire the first empire. Persians followed suit. invading Greece. The Greeks then taught the Romans the effectiveness of the horse in warfare. The Roman Empire was finally destroyed by the Goths, mounted on the heavy horse, now indigenous to mid-Europe.

The early immigrants to Scotland, arriving by boat, assuredly brought horses with them. They would not intend to attempt to settle in this foreign land, with its difficult terrain. without ensuring themselves of a reliable beast of transport. Early Scottish horses, therefore, almost certainly included some from the Scandinavian countries brought by Vikings who were probably the most frequent visitors to Scotland's shores. These migrant adventurers were certainly very competent travellers who would find no difficulty in adapting to the geography and climate typical of the Highlands and Islands of Scotland. They would also find appreciative people to tend and to utilise their horses. The Nordic horses as individuals would be added to the main equine population indigenous to Scotland, having had various components in its family tree.

The Celtic migration itself had brought to Scottish shores horses which had been carried by the great trek through Europe, ultimately to the northern and western limits of the continent, notably the Highlands and Hebrides. They brought a hardy pony of an undifferentiated type, and one obviously suited to the agrarian culture of the Celtic people. It is clear that the various forms of primitive horses were associated with specific regions of the broad European continent. To the east of the continent, in Mongolia, a primitive horse existed. That horse is now named the Przewalski horse, an equine species which has been successfully preserved after reaching the brink of extinction. Specimens of this species of prehistoric horse are maintained in zoos over the world.

In Central Europe the primitive horse form was the Tarpan. Although this horse seemingly became extinct several decades ago, Polish scientists succeeded in capturing wild horses in that area of

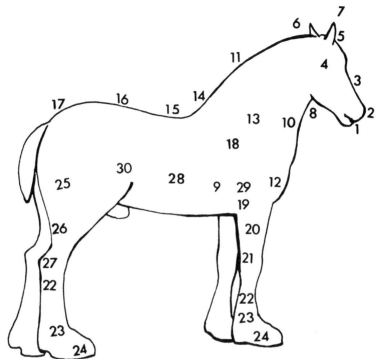

1 Mouth. 2 Nose. 3 Face. 4 Eye. 5 Forehead. 6 Poll. 7 Ears. 8 Throat. 9 Girth-/Heart. 10 Neck. 11 Crest. 12 Breast. 13 Blend of neck with shoulder. 14 Withers (Point at which height is measured in "hands", 1 hand = 4 inches or 10 centimeters). 15 Back. 16 Loins. 17 Croup/Tail head. 18 Slope of Shoulder. 19 Elbow. 20 Forearm. 21 Knee. 22 Cannon/Shank. 23 Fetlock. 23–24 Pastern. 24 Hoof. 25 Thigh. 26 Gaskin. 27 Hock. 28 Belly. 29 Triceps Muscle. 30 Stifle.

Points of the horse (silhouette of 'The Baron')

Europe which evidently contained strong traits of the Tarpan. By careful selective breeding, they managed to re-establish a horse which is essentially Tarpan. It is preserved now as a protected species. Both the Przewalski and the Tarpan are considered to represent the early forms of the warm-blooded horse, strains of which include the modern Thoroughbred and its close cousin, the Arabian. The latter, of course, is the elder breed and is the blend of many types which had their earliest origin in Mediterranean countries.

Descendants of the other principal form of the primitive horse can be found through the remainder of the horse world today. These are the cold-blooded horses, which have two forms. Most typical are the heavy draught horses which appear to have evolved in Western Europe, particularly in France and the Low Countries. The other smaller form is characterised by the Nordic horse which has a variety of types, each having certain similar features. These are found throughout many countries of Northern Europe from Iceland, Scotland and Norway through Sweden, Finland and into Russia.

A clearer picture has lately emerged of the way in which the Highland Pony's history apparently progressed. It is fairly certain that the pony was established as a primitive breed in Scotland before the country was properly inhabited by mankind. This horse, however, was not the same as the modern Highland Pony, which is a mosaic of several early types and blood lines which have come together. Thus the component foundations of the Highland Pony come from several ancestral sources, giving it mixed ancestry. The basic ingredient, however, of this animal is evidently Nordic, still very pre-potent, and providing it with its principal characteristics.

By tracing Nordic strains of horse breeds across Europe we find noticeable similarities in colour, morphology, temperament and behaviour. As we search the accepted route of equine migration from central Siberia, the origin of the Nordic strain appears to be the Yakut horse which is located in the valley of the river Yana in the central part of northern Russia, but its territory extends widely and even includes the polar circle to the north, containing some of the coldest regions of the northern hemisphere. Also included in the homeland are grasslands to the south which have deep snowfalls in winter and short. hot summers. The Yakut horse is an excellent pack animal. It is also used by local people in recreation, is a competent racer and is also used in a variety of equestrian games. The horse varies in size and is approximately of the same height and weight as the Highland Pony. The usual colours of the Yakut horse are reported to be light-grey, greyish or mouse-coloured. Some have dark, latticed patterns on their shoulders, and the eel stripe can be found along its back. These, of course, are the classical colours and markings of Nordic horses in general.

Traces of this kind of pony can be found not only from the Yana valley, but also in some parts of Europe. In Western Russia, which has been the location of so many wars, this horse is reported to have vanished. Earlier forms of warfare took a colossal toll of horses. Following wartime it was usual practice not to re-establish the horse population using the same native breeds but to attempt to establish

SKELETON OF THE HORSE

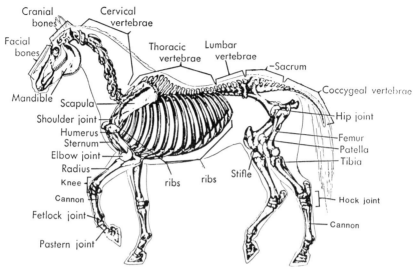

Skeleton of the horse

newer breeds locally by introducing foreign blood stock. These were often selected from quite distant countries in order to establish more distinctive breeds of horses of more desired characteristics. Such policies removed relics of the indigenous horse types of that expansive region of northern central Europe.

In Poland there is the Konik breed which is usually over thirteen hands high and is described as being more of a horse than a pony. The Konik is known to be able to thrive and work hard on a meagre diet. This makes it popular with the small farmers in Poland and throughout the adjacent parts of Eastern Europe. It is also noted for its robust constitution and its very amiable and quiet temperament. When the Konik horse is studied on the hoof some similarities to the Highland Pony are inescapable. It has the same compactness of build, the set of the neck and head, as the Highlander. It carries a long, thick mane and tail with silver streaks throughout these; a common colour is mouse dun. The legs are usually dark.

Another prominent member of this equine line is the Finnish horse. bred from ponies native to that country for innumerable centuries. These ponies are very similar to others still to be seen in other parts of Scandinavia where various types and sizes exist. A common colour is mouse-dun, with a silver mane and tail also being a colour feature.

9

The Native Horses of Scotland

In Scandinavia, one can pick out a Nordic horse in the form of the Northland breed. According to tradition, the ancestors of the present Northland horse were introduced from Russia over a thousand years ago. Very little original information exists about this early horse but it is clear that it was a small animal, sufficiently small to be called a pony. It was used for riding and for draught work in northern Scandinavia for hundreds of years. A neighbouring breed of horse is the North Swedish horse which is also very closely related to certain Norwegian horses.

The Gudbrandsdale is a northern Scandinavian breed of horse native to the eastern coast of Norway, although distributed throughout the whole country. It is very similar to Swedish and Finnish native ponies in physical capacity and conformation generally, but variable in size, often being larger than pony-size. They are usually dun in colour with a black dorsal stripe. They carry long manes, tails and fetlock feathers. Hardiness is a feature of the breed.

The Dole horse of Norway is a very handsome breed. It shows many of the characteristics of the Highland Pony but also some conspicuous differences. Probably it more resembles the British Dales breed of pony. Nevertheless, there are features in this breed reminiscent of the garron, such as the size, colour and elegant shape of head. A common colour is bay. Another close relation of these horses, having its place in the family tree of the Nordic strain, is the Fjord pony of Norway. It has been an inhabitant of Norway since prehistoric times. Vikings are known to have kept and bred this type of pony, and there are prehistoric carvings in stones which show essentially similar forms of horses over a wide area of Norway. The smaller Fjord pony is now the most popular and is well suited for the work on its own terrain. The Fjord pony is small and stocky, has a thick-set neck with a well-set head, small pricked-up ears, short back, strong hind quarters and a deep chest. A most common colour is dun with a dorsal stripe.

Nearer to home, the Icelandic pony is a close cousin to the Highlander but has a much less complicated history. It is generally believed that the ancestors of these ponies were not indigenous to Iceland, having been introduced by the original settlers from Norway in the ninth century A.D. The Icelandic pony is generally small, standing between twelve and thirteen hands. It is usually used for riding and has an amble in its gait. These short and stocky animals are noted for their good disposition and hardiness in living outdoors in severe weather.

The late Professor Ewart of Edinburgh was tempted to speculate that there must have been a prototype pony which he called *Equus celticus*. He claimed this to have been the common ancestor of all the pony breeds of northern Europe. The claim may have been too expansive. It might be reasonable to speculate on the existence of a Celtic pony of an earlier primitive type, but specimens of horses which can be examined today in various northern countries clearly indicate that the Nordic was the basic type of primitive horse to be found here. Doubtless, it was well-appreciated by many of the peoples who subsequently came to inhabit these various countries.

The careful sculpture of prehistoric carvings found in Norway and in Scotland clearly indicates the reverence these early peoples had for the horse. Indeed, it comes as no great surprise to learn that the earliest indication of the use of the side saddle for women appears on a carving on a Pictish stone in northern Scotland, dated about 800 A.D. The carving is a monument showing a Pictish lady of culture, possibly a princess, riding side saddle on a pony of Nordic, cold-blood, type.

Preserved in rocks and embedded within fossils is the evidence that Scotland is a very ancient habitation. Cave dwellers existed in the early periods of habitation as people who hunted and fished; stoic people who survived amidst the hardships, the climate and the hunger. Later there was a primitive, neolithic population of mixed European and Scandinavian origins. Relics of ancient deep-sea-going boats have been found in the estuaries of Scottish rivers; boats which date prehistorically. These immigrant people brought the Bronze Age to the Scottish lands. About this time Britain's location on the globe may have altered slightly. This geographical shift, however slight, appears to have been sufficient to modify the Scottish climate, making it more temperate, bringing great stretches of forest to the northern Highlands and some Islands and encouraging the lush growth of summer grass in meadows and glens. The climate became stable and the land more habitable. Early migrant man settled now in great numbers in this land. It cannot be stated accurately who the initial immigrants were. The only certainty is that they were of diverse origin from Western Europe and Scandinavia.

The earliest reliable account of the early immigrants to Scotland is of the Celtic civilisation which moved from central Europe westwards towards the Atlantic coast, into Brittany and Spain; across the sea to the Cornwall peninsula; northwards through Wales and Ireland and finally settling throughout the broad expanse of the Highlands and western coastline of Scotland, the outer limit of Europe. This Celtic migration extended over a long period of time and carried with it its own Celtic civilisation as it spread westwards. Its active migration is estimated to have occurred in the sixth century B.C. Within three more centuries the force of the Celtic migration had reached Scottish shores, and from that point of history onwards this Celtic race and the remnants of its culture have formed a basic fabric in Scotland's population. Characteristics commonly observed among Scottish people are still attributed to the Celtic race. The early Celts were described as high-spirited, frank, with a keen sense of honour but traits of barbarous savagery and much given to religion, philosophy and poetry. In addition, according to the writing of Caesar, they were warriors who used horses with skill.

The culture of this people had an artistic element. Innumerable relics have been found of Celtic jewellery in the form of fine silver brooches, gold pins, jewelled rings—many of these with elaborate ornamentation. Further archaeological findings include artifacts such as decorated pots, weaving combs, wooden writing tablets, metal styluses as writing instruments, leather tents, tools for carpentry and agriculture. Significantly, there were items for horse-shoeing, harnessing, and wooden carriage wheels. Clearly these people were not only a cultured and organised race but they were an agrarian people who used horses and horse power.

Celtic culture is shown by archaeological findings to have followed progressive pastoral development. The communities settled permanently in localities of their own. Within these regions they used local resources, evidently grazing livestock on available grasslands. They established permanent buildings, using stone, and erected stone monuments of uncertain significance, but evidently relating to symbols of their emerging culture. A form of rural civilisation was being pioneered in these settlements studded throughout the country. These small independent communities did not use slave labour and in their ambitious stone-shifting enterprises would probably find answers in horse power. All these progressive developments in which they adanced their culture took place over several centuries.

Ninth-century carved stones in theNorthern Highlands showed the inhabitants as competent horsemen mounted on well-built but medium-sized horses. They also possessed very sophisticated and decorative armoured headshields for their horses, of very finely beaten bronze. Some of these items are variously dated between 200 B.C.

and 800 A.D. The stone illustrations and the nature of the armoury indicate these horses probably drew the war chariots of the Celtic chieftains.

In 80 A.D., thirty-seven years after their conquest of England, the Roman legions first advanced into Scotland. The people of Caledonia arrested their progress and held them south of the Highland Line. This is the term which now defines that major geological fault north of Stirling, running diagonally north-east to south-west, making a mountain range with several distinguished Bens. There has always been a Highland Line of a metaphorical nature above the waist of Scotland, for the Highlands and Islands have always maintained some form of social boundary between themselves and the remainder of mainland Britain. About this time, Scotland's population became recognisable in two main groups, the Picts and Scots. In partnership they held the Roman legions at bay. Of these two groups, the Picts were probably the ones most representative of the earlier aboriginal inhabitants of northern Scotland, the very early Bronze Age colonists. Much of Scotland's history in the post-Roman era concerns the negotiations between them to live in harmony and to form one common nation, largely of Caledonian identity.

Caesar gave a description of Caledonians as a remarkably hardy race, capable of enduring fatigue, cold and hunger. They were decidely a war-like people; in battle they often made use of cars or chariots which were drawn by horses of a small, swift and spirited description.

Tacitus, in describing the last great battle which the Caledonians fought with Agricola near the passes of the Grampians, states that their first line was in the plain, and the next on the sloping ascent of the mountains, and that the space between the armies was filled with the cavalry and charioteers rushing to and fro with loud noise. They rushed, he tells us, in their armed chariots at full speed, and mixed in battle with the infantry. The horses of the country, it is certain, must have been numerous when they formed the strength of an army in a country so wild and mountainous. Whatever the character of these early horses with respect to size, strength, and other properties, it is probable that for many ages they had undergone little change.

Caledonian peoples learned certain Roman styles of living and some Roman skills, including equestrian skills, during eras of peaceful co-existence with the Romans. Periods of peacefulness were short-lived, for the Caledonians avoided coming to a general agreement with the

Roman emperors and kept up harassing warfare against the occupation forces. It was clear that the people north of the Roman defences were involved in agriculture. Like farmers the world over, they had an independent spirit; it could not be broken by Roman aggression. Indeed, they turned from a defensive to an offensive attitude when faced with the numerous attempts by the Romans to occupy their country. As a result, Hadrian's Wall was built by the Romans across Britain to prevent the Caledonians of the northern part of the country from invading the Roman provinces. Later Antonine's Wall was built from Forth to the Clyde, again erected defensively by Romans as another Scottish limit. More than one Roman Emepror attempted to extend the boundaries of his Empire to include all of Scotland; none succeeded and some died of the exertions. More than one legion of experienced Roman soldiers became swallowed up in vain attempts to occupy the Northern part of Scotland. Romans used cavalry in these invasive attempts. With their defeats, many of their horses would undoubtedly be left in the field to be captured, to be used and mixed with the indigenous horses.

After the Roman confrontations, the era which followed was by no means one of complete national harmony in Scotland, and subsequent centuries saw times of great violence and confusion over changing boundaries. Finally in 843 A.D. the Picts and Scots united under one King, Kenneth MacAlpine. He inherited a country well able to defend itself, peopled with competent agrarians and soldiers, who used the horse in the fields and in battle. In the background throughout this time, it is clear that the horse of the Scots was of critical importance in the development of the country.

At the time when Scotland's independence as a sovereign nation was established after Bannockburn, the country probably possessed a large population of general-purpose horses, suitable for riding, drawing vehicles, and working on the land, horses that would be small enough to keep economically and to be worked by all the members of the family engaged in the small farming units, some of which composed crofting communities.

During later centuries very significant hostilities took place throughout the length and breadth of the Highlands of Scotland. For example, it is reported that in a confrontation between the Earl of Argyll and the Earl of Erroll, the latter quickly engaged a select body of about a hundred horsemen, being gentlemen 'on whose courage and fidelity he could rely'. The forces grew after this point and it is said that nearly 1500 men, almost all mounted, were mustered under the rebel Earls of Huntly, Erroll and Angus to oppose the advance of Argyll. Huntly received intelligence that Argyll was on the eve of descending from the mountains to the lowlands, which led him the following day to send a party of horsemen to reconnoitre the enemy. Their findings encouraged Huntly and his men to attack Agryll after he had passed Glenlivet. Argyll was taken by surprise and, apprehensive that his numerical superiority and foot soldiers would be no match for Huntly's cavalry, he disengaged. He then awaited greater cavalry forces to join him, realising in his wisdom that horse forces in significant number were an essential part of a victorious army in the Highlands.

This military incident, only one of very many hundred military aggressions which characterise Scottish history, took place in May 1594. Huntly's smaller army was thrown into the battle, their hopes mainly dependent on the power of their cavalry which charged the enemy, causing wild confusion and flight. The lesson was there to be learned, but it is doubtful if it was driven home. During the remainder of Scottish history it is not evident that particular emphasis was placed on the force of cavalry to support the fierce aggression of the Highland foot soldiers. This particular incident, apart from the evidence it provides of the value of cavalry in warfare, was also an indication of the quantity of horse power which was available throughout most areas of united Scotland, both for warfare and agriculture.

2. Days of Horse Power

Horses have always looked well on the High Street in Edinburgh's Old Town as they have clattered down it with high-legged action or pulled up it with necks handsomely arched. From the Scots Greys, Scotland's cavalry regiment, to the Household Cavalry of modern monarchs, troops of horses have made good use of the cobblestones of this route between the Castle esplanade and the vast parade fields behind Holyrood, the official Scottish residence of the British monarch. Great institutions are based along this way. White Horse Close is one favoured courtyard of compact houses where a famous whisky was originally distilled and which once stabled the horses for the weekly coach run to London. The Castle, the High Street, the Canongate and the Palace of this Old Town represent the capital of a medieval European kingdom, still retaining many of the buildings of dignity and antiquity which give it its character. The Old Town's High Kirk of St Giles, its Parliament building dating back centuries, the intricacies of its back streets, closes and yards all give it an atmosphere which impresses a million visitors a year with genuine awe. The town is built of solid stone. From the quarries to the building sites the stone was of course transported by horses. The working horses of Edinburgh in that ancient period must have been an enormous army of animals. They spent their lives laboriously carrying quarried stones slung over their backs to collecting sites at the entrance of quarries where they were gathered into loads and put into carts which would be pulled into Edinburgh by traction horses working in tandem one in front of the other through narrow roads and lanes to be deposited at the site of each construction. One need only look today at the enormity of the stones which are typical of Edinburgh's construction to recognise the power of beast which went into this whole development. These horses are gone but it is still possible to reflect on them with interest and to appreciate what these animals did for early urban man in an age now rapidly receding into history.

When one looks at the stone sculpturing in Edinburgh, or in Glasgow's city centre—the crescents, the squares, the church spires, the civic buildings, the lavish monuments—one might imagine the sounds of thousands and thousands of hooves of tireless working

horses which made it all possible.

All travel had to be on horseback before carriages and coaches became commonplace between the towns and cities. Packhorses transported all heavy materials. These packhorses travelled in long trains numbering about twenty or more laden horses. Under the control of one horseman at the head, and another further down the line, the team of packhorses would be driven along the narrow crowns of the single-track roads which connected towns. Even in the middle of the eighteenth century coach traffic barely existed on the roads of Scotland. Travellers' reports of that era described the scene. Horse riders travelled upon a narrow causeway with an unmade soft side to the road on each side. From time to time strings of packhorses were encountered. This was the principal mode by which goods were transported around the countryside. The leading horse of the string carried a bell to give warning to travellers coming in the opposite direction. The causeway was often not wide enough to allow them to be passed easily when these trains of horses, with their very heavy packs slung across their backs, were met. Riders were obliged to make way for them and occasionally had to plunge down the soft side of the road. They sometimes found it difficult to get back up on to the causeway again. Post-chaises went out from certain towns to outlying districts to return with the same team of horses later in the same day. These carriage excursions were therefore of quite limited extent. Coaching between town centres started with relays of post-chaises using changes of horse.

The original proposals to run a coach between the towns of Glasgow and Edinburgh were drawn up in 1678. The agent who organised the initial coach service was William Hoon of Edinburgh who established it in a contract with the magistrates of Glasgow. This first service regularly plying between Glasgow and Edinburgh began on 1st September 1679 and ran for an initial period of five years. It began with one coach and six horses and it was suitable for carrying six persons with considerable baggage. Initially it travelled once weekly between the two cities but later ran twice a week and was guaranteed to run even if there were no passengers. In the summer season the return fare was eight shillings, the winter fare slightly more. The coach carrying passengers, baggage and the coach servants—as

Carriage travel: above and middle—traps, below—'Growler' or Brougham coaches at Charing Cross, Glasgow

they were called—set out from Glasgow on a Monday to return on the following Saturday night. The service was subsidised by the Provost and Bailies of Glasgow with occasional payments to Hoon for maintaining the service and for continuing to improve the design of the coach and its furnishings.

After the Union of Parliaments of 1707 and the dissolution of Parliament in Edinburgh the organisation of excursions to London required considerable planning. New carriages required to be built for the special purpose of conveying the members of deputations and, in order that the deputation might have some impact, everything was done in first-class style. Coaches for these special occasions could be built for twenty-eight pounds sterling in the year 1749. The type of coach favoured was a form of chaise, drawn by two horses. From Glasgow one went via Edinburgh. The first part of the journey to Edinburgh would take two days, from there to London eleven days. Mending of the chaise on the fierce roads would be required and horses would have to be frequently replaced along the way, so the whole excursion would eventually present a considerable expense. One such deputation from Glasgow to London sought relief to the town for the cost of certain repair work necessary in 1749 which amounted to four hundred and seventy-two pounds sterling. (Much civic damage had been left after Prince Charlie's visit, it was claimed.) Since the extent of the relief awarded to Glasgow as a result of this deputation was ten thousand pounds sterling, it can be seen that Glasgow knew how to bargain well with the bright new British Government in London. This was an indication that Glasgow would seek to ensure its own civic wellbeing through well-considered representation directly to London. It is possible that the keen business character of the city of Glasgow, as it is internationally recognised today, was formed in these early years as a result of such events and their lessons.

For many centuries, while the urban centres of Scotland were becoming established, much of the transportation of goods between towns, and between ports and inland markets, involved the use of packhorses. Even when wheeled transportation became more common during the eighteenth century, packhorses were still the preferred form of transportation of commercial goods, especially during

Coach types: above—stage coach, middle—Hansom carriage, bottom—Brougham coach the winter months when the road surfaces were deeply rutted in mud and unsuitable for carriage traffic. Throughout the eighteenth and nineteenth centuries many parts of the lowlands of Scotland were not provided with sufficiently good road-surfacing to permit transportation of goods by means other than packhorses bearing basket panniers. Each packhorse could carry two to three hundred pounds of goods from one town to another. As heavier draft horses were bred and became more abundant in Scotland, packhorse transportation became slightly more efficient, though still slow. There was nevertheless a progressive turn to wheeled transportation for people and goods from the eighteenth century onwards.

The first stagecoaches ran from London in 1640 but it was almost a century later before they came into regular use in Scotland. At first, travelling by coach was subject to considerable hazards. Quite apart from the discomfort of riding in vehicles, which did not have adequate springing, the prospect of the coach slipping from the road, overturning or otherwise breaking down in a remote part of the countryside made coach travelling not particularly attractive to many travellers. For this reason many able-bodied persons still preferred to travel on horseback.

From the Continent there came better-built coaches. In fact, the refinement of the coach as a fairly comfortable form of travelling was due to the skilled workmanship which went into the construction of these vehicles, notably in the town of Kocs in Hungary; from this the word 'coach' was derived. French coaches also came into more popular use. Whereas these seldom found their way directly to Scotland, Scottish coachbuilders were able to copy the refinements which had been achieved in coachbuilding on the continent of Europe. These more refined forms of coaches were very suitable for more rapid transportation, and a speed of ten miles per hour was possible. Stage and mail-coach services became established; mail coaches set the standard of travel for speed and comfort throughout Britain generally. The lowlands of Scotland, in due course, acquired a similar system.

By the middle of the nineteenth century the railway system was well introduced but there was less than a thousand miles of track in Britain at that time. Thereafter the expansion of the railway system brought about the end of long-distance travel and transport by horse-drawn vehicles. the railway stations served as focal points for transporters, and travellers required short-distance transportation by horse-drawn vehicles to the stations. This increased the local use of coaches and carriages.

The horse omnibus came into use in some areas so as to take substantial numbers of people from railway centres to adjacent towns which lacked railway services. Horse-drawn ombibuses, for example, were available in Princes Street in Edinburgh, adjacent to Waverley Station, at the end of the nineteenth century.

Coaches and carriages had their day during the eighteenth century. They became refined with features such as elliptical springs, greased axles, rubber tyres and upholstered seating. The commercial and the farm carts were robust, realiable vehicles with strong wheels, increasingly made through mass production and with precision. Two-wheeled carts and four-wheeled wagons were equally numerous on the town road and on the farm. The style of vehicle sometimes was determined according to the nature of the material which was carried. Farm wagons of the four-wheeled variety were in many cases secondhand carriages which had previously done service as vehicles for commercial goods. These four-wheeled wagons were all essentially similar in appearance, the main feature being a flat deck of boarding, iron-shod wheels, with the front pair small enough so that they could turn underneath the deck of the wagon when it was being turned sharply by swivelling the front axle. The difficulty of giving a good turning lock to the forecarriage in four-wheeled vehicles was often a problem in the construction of heavy wagons. Smaller wheels sufficiently reduced in size to pass under the vehicle were not particularly good on poor roads or deep mud and they reduced the draught potential of the wagon. For this reason, particularly when vehicles were being used on rough farm roads, two-wheeled carriages or carts became more popular. When such carts were being used on soft ground, as for example in farm work, the wheels were often made particularly large in diameter to improve the traction of the vehicle, to prevent it being bogged down in soft ground and to be more suitable for weight-bearing. Variations occurred in wheel breadth. In some cases narrow wheels were preferred, while in others broad wheels were thought to smooth out ruts and therefore improve the roads on which they were being used. Wheels not only created ruts but were extremely troublesome when they got lodged in them. The narrow wheel, however, was lighter in traction and allowed the use of a lighter horse which could move more briskly.

The problem of ruts was eventually solved by the Scot, Macadam,

who reinvented, so to speak, metal roads. Macadam's roads were far superior to anything that had ever been conceived of before, in the form of so-called 'metal surface', or roads surfaced with stone. Macadam used only small stones and it is claimed he spot-checked the suitability of size of stones used in his roadworks by seeing if those of average size could be placed in his mouth. The stones used, therefore, were mostly of plum to egg in size and shape to form a deep layer on the roads which he built. Macadam limited the steep gradients of his roads. Before his time roads were often built without regard to their steepness but the maximum gradient which he permitted was one in thirty. Macadam's roads, because of the nature of their surface, were resilient and they certainly allowed heavier carts to travel on them without suffering damage. Heavy vehicles could then be used on these roads and could also be drawn by suitable horse teams at faster speeds. On a Macadam-built road, vehicles with a laden weight of five to seven tons could be drawn at a speed of three miles per hour or more.

Vans and carts used by tradespeople and shopkeepers moved along every street in every town. Most of these were carts which had two wheels and were well sprung. They were usually well turned out also, being painted with the name of the trader and the description of his business. The wheels were attractively painted and the bodywork of the van or cart would be lined out, in many cases, with an attractive contrasting colour such as gold or red. In the nineteenth century the metal parts of such vehicles were considered to be part of their decor and increasingly these were made of nickel and brass so that they could be shined up. The horses, too, were selected for the type of use to which they would be put and also for their good appearance.

As horses became older they would change hands and would then find themselves being used in less attractive business on the street. Refuse and dung carts, carts carrying coal and timber for fuel could not be expected to compete aesthetically on the street with vehicles which delivered milk or vegetables or bakery products. Passenger vehicles were of course made the most attractive of all. These were used mainly by people of position such as doctors and clergymen who were anxious to present themselves publicly in a style which would reinforce the social status which they enjoyed. Increasingly the horse-

Family groups harvesting in the late nineteenth century with horse-drawn reaper. Note the high-peaked horse collars, typically Scottish

drawn passenger vehicle was used as a status symbol, as well as a fairly proficient means of transportation. In the twentieth century, prior to the first World War, horse-drawn vehicles were still being used privately for passenger transportation, mainly as a hallmark of social position. Even up to the start of World War II it was possible to observe an occasional doctor using horse-drawn vehicles such as gigs while on his rounds. Horse-drawn carriages emphasised the splendour of an occasion; being transported in a horse-drawn vehicle was an experience manifestly enjoyable.

The numerous prints and paintings of the coaching age provided abundant evidence of the way in which horses were the essential means of transportation for the civilised community. Great variations occurred in the types of coaches used and the teams of horses drawing them. A team might be a pair or it might be six horses; larger teams were rare and the private vehicle was usually drawn by one horse. Even hackney carriages available for hire, although drawn by a pair of horses at one time, were essentially one-horse vehicles by the time they had come into general use. The typical hackney was known as the 'growler'. The brougham was a similar type of coach, as was the clarence. These were all four-wheeled coaches having two doors with windows, the cabin being totally enclosed. The driver sat up in front. The hansom cab was also popular on the streets as a vehicle for hire. this cab was a two-wheeled vehicle with the driver sitting up behind the cab. The cabin was entered from the front and was not enclosed completely though it had a roof, back and sides. The front remained open and the passenger was usually obliged to wrap up in a travelling rug. All of these vehicles were finished off in considerable splendour with brass-fitted oil lamps sitting in their holder by the head of the vehicle, and they were drawn by stylish horses. The hackney carriage (which derived its name from the French word *haquenee*), and which was available for hire from a stand in the street, was typically drawn by a horse with stylish gait. High-stepping trotting horses were favoured, and as a result the hackney breeds both of horse and of pony were developed for the needs of this trade. The main characteristic of the hackney's gait is the very high elevation of the horse's knees as it moves at the trot. Hackney horses were used to draw the hansom cab most usually. Hackney ponies were developed from the same breed but were smaller in size and became more popular later, with privately owned vehicles of the two-wheeled variety such as gigs. These lightweight carts were usually owner-driven, but of a size suitable for

Working in traces on the highway, the field, the peat bog and Glasgow city centre

two persons, both facing forward. Other forms of lightweight, two-wheeled vehicles which became popular for private use included the governess cart, the dog cart, and buggies and gigs in general.

For the horses between the shafts of a 'growler' coach for hire, work was often tiresome and physically exhausting. They would often be left standing 'cold' at a rank awaiting a fare. When engaged for a journey around town it was often a hurried engagement. The driver would try to set off at a brisk pace to reassure his fare that his business was being taken seriously. Later the pace would be slackened to a slow trot, which these fit horses could maintain for an hour, quite easily. The brisk clip-clop of this two-beat gait would give a pleasant rhythm to the journey. A hackney carriage could offer relaxation as well as transport to a passenger!

In the busier streets of the town centres the horses would be limited to a walk as the coachman threaded a way through crossings, where anarchy reigned in the absence of any control of traffic. For a passenger in no great hurry, such circumstances could give an interesting picture of city life. From the detached and comfortable

27

B

position of a well-padded leather carriage seat a person could casually view life in its most frenetic form. Runners ran messages around town, as business gentlemen in white spats waddled and weaved across streets none too clean; ladies in voluminous dresses, possible with children at heel, sought to walk in the midst of a throng unwilling to give her the room that her station and attire seemed to warrant. Pedestrian traffic was thick and a coachman had to use just a little caution when ploughing through it, in the absence of formally appointed custodians of the law. There being no police at this time, mob rule was real enough and not to be provoked by running down an innocent—though accidents did happen.

The story has been heard of a very reverend minister's wife, attending a social function in Edinburgh during the week of the General Assembly of the Church of Scotland, who tried to hurry the coachman lest she arrive late. She asked the driver to whip the horse on the rump to a faster pace. Soon she asked him to whip it somewhere else to freshen the pace again. 'Madam,' he replied, 'I have whipped the horse everywhere but his testicles and I'm saving these for the High Street.'

In fact, nearly all hackney horses were geldings; these were most suited in temperament and behaviour to their chronic toil in the streets. When their service was nearly over they might be used on a nightshift, when fares were less numerous and the quieter streets easier to travel with fewer changes of pace. At the end of their hackney career when their legs and feet became sorely troubled with ring bone, splints, spavin, navicular disease, or any combination of these, they were put into semi-retirement as 'hacks'. The work would then be much easier, probably on softer bridle paths, burdened only with an occasional rider, none too athletic.

To earn its way into hackney service a horse had to be tall, sound of wind and limb, well broken to street work and have a good way-of-going. The exaggerated style of hackneys was more favoured by owner-driven carriages. The carriage for hire was often too demanding in its work for a horse with a prancing gait. On one trip the most common type of hackney carriage—the growler—might carry one person on a short trip of three or four street blocks; on the next it might hold a whole Victorian family on a visit to the far side of town. The growler could hold quite a number of passengers, though four would be considered its full complement. It was of such good overall design and function that it virtually put all other forms of carriage for

Commercial horse traffic on Glasgow streets

hire off the street, with the exception of the lighter, smaller, two-wheeled, versatile and fast vehicle—the hansom cab. A horse of the hackney breed could cope nicely with this. In this vehicle the passenger was more exposed to the elements and required a travelling rug since the face of the cab was open above the dash (or splash) board. The driver handled the reins from a high seat situated above and behind the small two-seater cab. The typical stage coach was a four-wheeled, two-door, enclosed coach driven by a man sitting up on a box outside the coach and located high above the splash board which formed a foot-well for the driver and one other coach attendant. The second man in the driving seat was usually 'the whip' who needed skill in distributing encouragement appropriately to the team members needing it. Stage coaches, so favoured also in nineteenth-century America, in order to carry their heavier load at the canter, used teams of pairs. Many teams were made up of two pairs; long-distance coaches with experienced drivers used three pairs. The London coach leaving White Horse Close in Edinburgh each week had a team of six. When a team of three pairs drew a coach they were harnessed so that the leading pair had taut reins and slack traces (the long leather straps connecting the collar to the point of the vehicle's central pole). This allowed the leaders to be guided. The central pair had a reverse form of harnessing, with slack reins and taut traces—so as to concentrate their energy on pulling. The two 'wheelers', close to the front two wheels of the vehicle, were harnessed like an ordinary pair with reins and traces well engaged.

It became the custom for the coachman to drive these larger teams (a few consisted of eight or even ten horses) from the box and to dispense with postilion riders. Postilions rode on the nearside horse in the leading pair and the wheeling pair. Postilions certainly had greater control of the team than a single driver with fistfuls of reins. But it was a hazardous job being a postilion rider (they could take a fall) and their use was eliminated in teams which moved at speed, though they were still useful on teams moving sedately: drawing state coaches, for example.

Driving had its own techniques. The leading horse pulled on the driver's hand through direct reins, and since these horses were seldom 'in the collar', because of their slack traces, they could remain fresh and set the pace for the whole team. The central pair in a team of six pursued the leaders but their thrust was into the collar and their pull therefore on the traces, not on the reins in the coachman's hands.

The short reins for the wheelers put only a limited pull on the driver. As a result of this method of reining a driver did not need to exert great force in piloting a properly harnessed large team. Providing he held his wrists supple and bent, and kept each elbow close into his side, the coachman's use of the reins could be light.

The whip was employed in quite specific ways. A long flying lash was usually unnecessary since it was not normally needed on the leaders— and could not always pick them out accurately in any event. The four horses closest to the coach could be lightly touced with the whip in truly professional style. All four horses in succession could be made to feel a wipe of the thong in one skilful side-to-side sweeping stroke. The blinkers on the bridle of every horse protected eyes from a careless lash. A driver was mainly judged on the way his horses stretched their harness, ensuring that each horse did its share of the work. This was an important feature of the start as well as the long haul. A bad start caused jibbing and balking.

In breaking a young horse into a team he was usually paired with an old 'stager'. The latter did the work of starting, by driving his weight into the collar. As the pupil horse got the feel of the collar and got the confidence to pull his weight, the old stager would begin to hang back, little by little, his traces becoming more slack as the novice's became taut in a youthful zeal for running. The youngster, when he had learned to vent his instinctive drive to go places by shoving his energies into the collar, was then assured a working life on the road.

The governess cart was low-built with a single small door at the rear and high sides all around. Inside the cart or car two padded benches faced each other. Some form of decorative rail ran round the top of the cart, for the vehicle was essential for the transportation of young children under the care of the governess—the full-time, professional 'babysitter' of that era. The dog cart, another lightweight two-wheeled vehicle for private use, although originally used to transport sporting dogs, ceased to have that function when this vehicle became popular on the streets. It was an open vehicle without any hood. Its main characteristic was that the seats were set back to back, and it was usually built to carry four persons. The buggy, another lightweight vehicle, also had a hood and had a rear seat for two behind the driver's seat facing forward. The American version of the buggy was basically similar although it was a four-wheeled vehicle. The advantage of a low cart such as the governess cart was obvious in that it allowed easy loading and ease of entry for the less than athletic person. Such vehicles were sometimes referred to as floats. Luggage and game floats were used in excursion work. Later some floats were found suitable for transporting large livestock since they could be loaded on to these with relative ease.

The cart in its many forms was essential to the development and maintenance of business in the towns. The streets of Scotland thronged with them throughout the nineteenth century. Even up to the outbreak of World War II all the towns and cities of Scotland were well supplied by goods that were transported throughout the streets by cart. Carts pulled by heavy draft horses and lightweight ponies were commonplace. Four-wheeled vans for the transportation of materials that required enclosure, such as bakery products, used tall horses, called vanners. They were not a specific breed although they were quite a special type. Although not heavyweight animals, they had adequate height and strength to draw these vehicles along at a brisk pace throughout a full day of work on the town streets. The vanner was one of the more common types of horse on Scottish streets until 1940. Today it is completely gone from our midst. No doubt horses of this type could be bred again although it is doubtful if there are many breeders with the knowledge to blend the numerous characteristics of varying breeds of horse so as to produce the traits of that particular type of animal. The nearest one can come today to horses of that type is in the hunter class of animal although vanners were cold-blooded horses while hunters (e.g. police horses) usually have hot blood in them via the Thoroughbred. Possibly the last type of horse to be seen in fairly large numbers on the streets of Scotland was the one that drew the merchant's cart, for the delivery of goods by horse-drawn carts was still fairly common practice up to 1950.

The citizens acquired the domestic essentials from the merchant's carts; most grocery requirements, for example, would be available at a regular time of the day, or week, in every street of every town. Coal carts were numerous. With the production of coal in Scotland at such a high level, it was used quite freely in most homes for heating and cooking. The competition in the streets between coal merchants became quite keen at times and took the form of what are now more commonly called 'price wars'. The coal merchants travelled the streets, calling out the price of their coal. If they had managed to reduce the price by a halfpenny a bag, this was the selling point which they cried out at the top of their voices so that all could hear. Even families living in high and remote corners of tenement buildings were

Heavy horse traffic on Glasgow bridges (early twentieth century)

usually able to hear the loud cries of coal merchants advertising the latest price of their coal laden on their carts in hundredweight bags.

The trace horses of Glasgow, standing by the pavement edge, were fondly noticed by most of the million citizens on city business. These horses were usually old geldings, pensioners in fact. They still earned their daily rations being coupled, in tandem, to the shafts of a heavily laden cart which had only one horse, quite unable, for instance, to take the long slope up to Buchanan Street railway station. They were a feature of Glasgow whose kind citizens would usually note the animals appreciatively and stop occasionally to pat one or offer a titbit, with the permission of their drivers standing against the wall, awaiting a horse and cart in need. The trace horses had seen better days and were a little bit withered with a combination of age and a life of hard work, but they had presence and they were loved in their time, in this no mean city.

The Clydesdale in town work did not wear as well as his country cousins, for the work was hard and quite relentless. Clydesdales were old by nine years and were often 'pensioned' then. A pension might be a few more years of easier, lighter work away from pounding hard streets daily. Sometimes their bones—prematurely aged—would be left with outgrowths, making them chronically lame and unfit, so they would go to an early end at the slaughterhouse on the east side of Glasgow.

The railways used many Clydesdales, usually the best, in the depots where trucks would be shunted about to form a goods train. Even empty, these trucks were of considerable tonnage and they needed great horse power to move them. This was the heaviest work any horse could get; it broke the health and spirits of some. At the end of World War II there were about two hundred railway horses (all Clydesdales, of course) in the Glasgow area. Their principal stable, and hospital, was centrally located on Parliamentary Road. By 1951 the stable had sixty horses, and by 1952 it was empty and closed. a great era had passed and ended under the noses of an unwitting populace, whose next generation would never see these handsome heavy horses, so huge of heart, abounding in their native metropolis.

3. Highland Pony Affairs

The eighteenth century was a very important time in the history of the Highland pony. This was a testing time, the century of its consolidation. It was uniform in type now and featured very many desirable characteristics, both physical and temperamental. Prominent features included hardiness to withstand the rigorous climate of the north and west, strength for draughtwork, stamina for long spells of toil. Docility and a compliant temperament were also needed.

The form of micro-farming, which we refer to as crofting, requires horse power of a very appropriate type. It was no mere coincidence that the appropriate type was to hand. The work on these small portions of arable land very often required that a single horse be used. The need was for a horse of medium build but of great strength to cope with the rocky subsoil; a horse so highly domesticated that it could be used by man, woman or child, with complete safety and proficiency; a horse so versatile in its uses that there was no task for which it was not capable. The chores of the Highland pony within this culture were extremely varied. Peat was the form of fuel used in cooking and in heating the sheilings. This peat required to be dug in bogs quite often far removed from these habitations. Pony power was required to transport the peat across stony lands to the homesteads in order to supply domestic fuel the year round.

In the springtime the animals would be needed for ploughing. Arable land was often in confined areas with intricate contours—a thin subsoil over rock. Seaweed, as fertiliser, had to be carted from the shore at low tide. Subsequent harrowing of ploughed land again would use the peculiar skills of the Highland pony—stamina, courage, power, manoeuvrability and compliance. At harvest the cutting of hay and of corn did not need horse-drawn machinery, as a rule, since the cutting was done by hand. Nevertheless, horses were used to draw carts on which hay and corn was carried to the stackyard, close by the house for convenience during the winter for feeding livestock. Some of the draughtwork of these animals was done using panniers of wickerwork, draped one on either side of the animal. Sometimes the vehicles being drawn by the animals were wheeled carts, sometimes they would be sledges. On other occasions they would be a very peculiar type of wheelless cart or slide car consisting of two long poles which were dragged behind the horse along the ground; across these poles would be built a hod with a floor and a back of wood to carry sufficient supplies of peat. Occasionally the horses would be used to draw carriages of families who were visiting far from home, families who were attending some special social event.

Ponies provided regular transportation for the mobile people in the community—physicians, traders, landowners. They were also used for riding, but by and large they were not used for this purpose excessively. In the main the crofters conserved the horse and saved its legs as much as possible. They chose to walk with their animals, rather than ride them over rough ground. When they were ridden they were generally taken at a slow pace. Again this was an effort to extend the life of the animal as a member of the work force. This was no indication that the animal did not make a good mount. It has long had a vigorous gait and the ability to move freely.

Although stallions were certainly docile enough throughout most of the year to be hand-led by almost anyone, their breeding value was recognised to be of critical importance and their work was usually limited to this. Mares were used for breeding for much of the time and would be occasionally used for riding. They would certainly be used in harvest work and ploughing, even if pregnant. The ponies which did most of the more strenuous work were the geldings. The Gaelic word to describe a castrated horse is 'garron'. For this reason, the garron was the most common form of word for the Highland pony. The name in due course became applied to the breed in general, particularly by non-Gaelic-speaking people who came to recognise the breed and came to appreciate it.

The emasculation, or cutting, of the males was particulary neces- sary for the demands of spring work. Using the daylight characteris- tics for its calendar, the Highland pony has probably a shorter breeding season than ponies indigenous to lighter, more southern latitudes in Britain and elsewhere. For this reason there is a more defined breeding season, in the late spring of the year. While this breeding activity is concentrated, entire ponies are extremely active and alerted for breeding. With a little stretch of the imagination, their behaviour at this time can be seen to resemble the rut which accom- panies breeding in deer, in the same latitudes. Throughout the remainder of the year, the sex drive of entire Highland ponies presents no real trouble. If they retain one male characteristic throughout this time it is that they are less tolerant of chronic tedium than their castrated brothers, the true garrons.

The work of the garron did not end with crofting. He was an animal frequently used by cattle drovers who were a very distinguished group of cattlemen in the Highlands. They were given special privileges in law, giving them the right to carry weapons and to wear tartan, the dress which was banned for decades in Scotland by the British government. Young men who had been allowed into the fraternity of drovers were considered to have risen in society. Native Gaelic speakers, they were of course required to speak in English also since their work mainly concerned the transportation of large numbers of cattle on the hoof from the north of Scotland down into England. This journeying also brought them into contact with a wider spectrum of society in the course of which they acquired some of the manners and habits of the gentry in cities and townships to the south. Mounted drovers wore trews and these long, tartan, close-fitting trousers of proper Highland riding habit became popularized in southern Scotland. There they have been worn as uniform by Scottish regiments since. On their return from season-long drives of cattle, drovers would be welcomed in their home townships where they would entertain their relations and neighbours with tales of their travels and news from the south. Their influence on society was substantial.

Drovers moved cattle on the hoof, from the Highland areas of cattle production to the urban centres of consumption. They would begin their drive from places as distant as Ardnamurchan, Skye and Dingwall. Their journeys would end at Crieff or Falkirk. The Crieff Tryst, as it was called, was a colossal meeting of drovers, butchers, dealers and graziers engaged in private trading. Auctioneers were not used and most deals were struck through personal trust between drover and buyer, based on reputation.

In the eighteenth century as many as 150,000 head of cattle per year were driven from all corners of the Highlands and Islands down the glens and along the drove roads to Lowland markets. From here they went on to Glasgow, Edinburgh and the North of England. Cattle were then the principal wealth of the Highlands, being the chief trade and cash source. In time Falkirk became the main centre for the industry: 24,000 head of cattle were sold there in 1772, and this figure increased to an average of 50,000 per year; towards the end of the century it reached a peak with 150,000 cattle and 100,000 sheep. The annual

assembly of these animals covered the land for miles in every direc-
tionl direction. A site of 200 acres was fenced in for the actual business
transactions and the scene there in 1849 was described as one 'to
which certainly Great Britain, and possibly the whole world, does not
offer a parallel. All is animation, bustle, business and activity'. People
ran about, shouting and directing cattle. In addition to drovers and
buyers, there were gamblers, peddlers, jugglers, beggars, singers,
hawkers, bankers and pickpockets. By 1890 the trade started to die off
as other centres developed in Oban, Inverness and Aberdeen, where
animals could be transported by the railway system, which put an end
to the skilled activity of droving.

Much preparation for the drove would involve the pony. Over a
saddle would be placed a small, well-padded wooden tressle. Upon
this would be fixed the numerous items essential to the drover on his
long journey. A bag of coarse oatmeal would be a necessity, not only to
feed the drover himself, but also to supply the pony with extra
nourishment from time to time, especially on the return journey.
When the drover had finished his business he would ride much of the
way home, without too much time to graze the pony while trying to
beat the winter.

Some essential cooking items would be added to the pack. More
than one blanket would be rolled up and bound onto the pads. At least
one plaid would also be included with an extra pair of boots, for much
of the southbound journey would be on foot; drovers knew the
wisdom of sparing their garrons for as much of the journey as possible.
With a heavy stoneware jug of whisky secured, the whole pack would
be draped with a sheepskin. The drover would set off leading his
garron on a rope halter with a long shank which allowed the pony to
follow behind. With his dog and his stick he would direct the course
the cattle would take down the long glens that led to the grasslands of
the south. One drover could manage about twenty head. Bigger
droves of cattle numbering over a hundred head would be driven by an
experienced man with the help of younger men willing to work on foot
as directed, eager to enjoy the adventure and learn the trade. Smaller
droves were more usual, for drovers preferred to work alone. They
also found it easier to get grazing for their animals—they stopped the
drive about the middle of the day and in the evening—when numbers
of cattle were limited. They might ride for the last hour of the drive in
the early evening astride the pack, and a drove could regularly cover
about ten miles per day without the stock losing condition. On the

return journey the drover would walk for the morning and ride in the later afternoon, to cover in comfort twenty miles per day and still enjoy some social activities in towns along the high road home.

As he travelled homewards the drover could accumulate packages of snuff, tobacco, tea and perfumes to take back to his own community for trading and for gifts. These commodities could be acquired in market towns. But along the east coast, where the European smuggling trade was active in fishing villages, bargains were better. Their concealment in the horse's pack was a simple matter. Once a light load of such contraband as a firkin of brandy was acquired a drover would make haste homeward.

On the final laps of the return journey the drover would ride his garron more often as he tired. The animal was then in the best of physical condition, hardened by the long excursion; he knew from the northern sky ahead and the feel of the sun on his rump when he was going homeward. His pace would quicken as he got among the hills and saw the mountains of his own heath. He would hear racing streams, the plaintive call of curlews, the screaming of gulls, the sounds of homeland. The nearer the journey came to its close, the stronger would be the pulling power of home. The smell of peat lands, the taste of Highland herbage, the crystal clear air, which carried smell and sound from afar, the feel of fine rain, they were all so familiar. The horse's ears would not cease moving in every direction and his nostrils would be held wide open to absorb all the signs of his own place on earth which his breed had endured in all the fortune and misfortune of Highland life.

On cold sharp spring mornings, with the ground sparkling with a light frost on it, crofters would rise earlier than usual and check that the weather was dry and suitable for ploughing. Then they would prepare their garrons for a day of hard work ploughing those parts of their crofts which were to be used that season for growing corn. Depending on the nature of the ground to be ploughed and the horses available, a pair might be chosen, or a lone garron would be given the job of drawing the plough. One horse would often by given the job on smaller crofts. The horse would have been stabled overnight to be available for an early start. He would be taken out of his stall and the bedding brushed off; his feet would be picked up and the wet bedding and manure, packed into the soles of the hooves overnight, would be scraped out. The animal would be led out of the stall by the forelock. The collar, turned upside down, would be pushed over the face and head of the pony and turned around before being settled down onto his shoulders. The bridle would then be fitted and the strap over the lack put in place to carry the traces upon metal hooks on each side. These traces would lead back from the collar to be fixed upon either end of a swingle tree, a wooden cross-piece to which was fixed a solid iron ring at its centre; to this the plough would be linked. Long fine ropes would be stretched as plough reins, from the bit on each side, passed over the hames—the iron yokes secured around the leather collar—then backwards, eventually to be carried in either hand of the ploughman while he manipulated horse and plough.

When the animal was suitably harnessed and the loose pieces gathered up, the horse would be walked to wherever the plough had been left lying from its previous use. The animal would be backed up close to the plough and harnessed to it. The crofter ploughman would then set out for the day's work, turning the plough on its side so that it might be dragged more easily by the pony to the place where the ploughing was to begin. As close to the edge of the field as possible, near some low drystone dyke, the man would line the horse up and urge him forward. The pony, doubtless recalling the whole purpose of the exercise from a previous occasion, would push his weight into the collar, drawing the plough quickly forward. The crofter would lift the handles of the small plough upwards so as to drive the tip of the ploughshare into the subsoil. In many cases the subsoil of the croft would be no more than a few inches deep. When the plough was down to its adequate depth the pony would be kept going forward at a steady, measured tread.

The first furrow was important. It was the line which the subsequent furrows would follow. The crofter would take a series of sightings ahead of the horse, guiding the animal from one to another and attempting to pursue a straight line. In certain circumstances ploughing on the croft demanded a different tactic. Furrows had to follow the contours of the rises and falls of a small croft field. This was important to prevent furrows acting as gutters for rapidly running water when heavy rains fell, flushing away precious soil. At the far end of the ploughing area the furrow would cease, and the crofter, by some skilful manoeuvring, would turn the horse around some few yards away from the initial furrow and set off in the direction he had come to make a second furrow going in the opposite direction. By passing up and down the field, the up furrows lying to one side and the down furrows to the other, segments of the ploughing area would be turned over and in the course of the morning perhaps a quarter of an acre would be ploughed. The work would end for the midday rest with a call and a wave from an aproned figure by the croft house.

Highland ponies make good ploughing animals; they enter into the spirit of the exercise. They do not respond to it unwillingly as though it were some chore, but the kinship with man, the apparent knowledge that they are participating in an important ritual seems to give them a style, a purpose, in which they fulfil themselves.

When ploughing, garrons will nod their heads, shaking loose their dense manes, and they will snort with satisfaction as they push into the collar. They lift their feet cleanly and dig their hooves into the earth, giving considerable horse power to the operation. As the day wears on and they become heated with work they will arch their tails, in a way that adds to their style, to cool themselves. Thin films of sweat appear on their bodies and the sides of their necks may become lathered. In this work, as in no other, the Highland pony is able to show his grit. With the crofter following behind his horse, giving adjustments in direction, manipulating the plough so as to take the right depth of soil and the right width of furrow, his respect for his animal would grow with the passing of the working day. The accomplishment of man and beast would be substantial in the work of ploughing an acreage of corn which, from previous calculations, could provide grain for man and beast throughout the winter after harvest.

At the end of the working day the plough would be uncoupled by the side of the field, the chains looped up to the harness, the long reins coiled and thrown over the hames, and the animal would be led back towards the stable. The walk back would be slow, allowing the animal to cool out. At the stable the harness would be removed, the crofter would stop and, snatching some old dry pieces of braken or some hay from the small stackyard by the stable, he would rub the animal down to dry him off. The brisk drying off would be the opportunity for communicating to the horse the crofter's affection for his animal. Soft Gaelic phrases would accompany this grooming. With the animal dried and cooled the crofter would lead his pony by the forelock to some brisk-running stream of mountain water where the animal would slake its thirst. The pony would then be led back to a grassy area within sight of the windows of the croft house. With a noose of a long tether slipped around the leg just above the hoof, he would be allowed to graze for a spell. At his own table, and while eating his own meal, the crofter would keep an eye on his pony grazing around the restricted circle of the tethered area. In a while the crofter would return to the animal, remove the noose from the foot and lead the pony back to the stall, putting down deep fresh bedding and throwing a sheaf of corn into its manger to give sufficient food for the night. The great day's work was ended and the new year of work for the horse, following the long wintertime holiday on the hillsides, was begun.

Days in the hayfield, in the best of summer, were long and filled with backbreaking work with sickle and scythe, rake and fork. After the haymaking had gone through its stages of cutting, turning and raking, haycocks in increasing size were built. Horses then joined the families of haymakers in the fields for the final work of loading the hay onto carts and gathering it in, close to the byre. This was the best time of the season, a happy time when the hay was finally dried and could be securely stacked to maintain the livestock for next year.

Cartwork, for a horse with a suitable build for it, is not the worst lot in life. It gives a horse an outlet for its basic urge to move, to keep its limbs in action and to generate one horsepower of energy. Carting comes as close as any other horse-game to the provision for a natural need of dynamic expression. When they are working within themselves horses of the right disposition can derive evident satisfaction from drawing carts. The boxcart had short shafts so that the animal was well coupled to its load. The box was very close to its hindquarters, sometimes sloping slightly over them to make the draught work a balanced mixture of pulling and carrying. Snugly harnessed in a boxcart, the Highland pony's long tail was a disadvantage. It could not be properly lifted when evacuating and so became soiled. It would get out of the breaching occasionally and could not be drawn in again by the animal, which found this irritating in time. A very lengthy tail could get in the way when the box was being released from the frame so as to be tipped up. When the emptied box was dropped back down again, a long tail could become painfully crushed. So the tail was cut or "docked" to a handspan in length when carting was the animal's destined lot.

The garron has a natural aptitude for deft cartwork. On the field he could be manoeuvred easily by man, woman, or child from one haycock to another as the load of hay was picked up. With well fitting harness, such as padded collar and saddle, the pony worked easily and willingly between the shafts of a hay cart, or a boxcart, when the animal could use his power. Negotiating a wheeled load by a difficult route was a test of manoeuvrability that was all in the day's work for a surefooted garron.

At the end of the day the pony would be led to the spot where the cart was always put up. He would be uncoupled from the shafts and these would be raised to let the horse out to be stabled and unharnessed. After this the several needs of the horse would receive the crofter's attention. The working horse needed watering, feeding, grooming, bedding and securing for the night. Before going to his own bed, the crofter would revisit the stable or trevis and while giving a further supply of feed, would take a few moments to run a hand over his animal appreciatively, giving him a hearty pat on the rump for the day's effort. From a normally undemonstrative keeper this gesture could be an adequate reward for a knowing garron, helping in another night of constraint. Later giving himself up to several hours of lying in the manmade bed, the pony would sleep, napping periodically through the night to be wide awake by dawn. By the arrival of the sunlit morning the pony would be recharged with vitality for another day between shafts, in the service of his people.

After the Jacobite rebellions of the eighteenth century and the clearances of the nineteenth, as well as human depopulation—at the start of the twentieth century the population was twenty-five per cent of what it had been a hundred years before—the depopulation of ponies was very substantial, but an attempt was made to sustain the breed by the Department of Agriculture for Scotland. By providing good-quality stallions to parishes and districts in the Highlands and Islands, pony breeding was still carried out. This was of great assistance in maintaining the breed in viable numbers. Not only did this policy maintain a critical level of equine population, but with the breeding of garrons now being done by stallions licensed by a Government Department there was an assurance that stallions of quality were in general use. At times there were complaints that some of the stallions sent by the Department to travel areas of the Highlands had some Clydesdale features in them. This was not desired by crofters and the animals never became popular. The crofting people still preserved the desired type in their Highland mares, and they had a keen eye for suitable stallions. Clerks of crofting townships where Highland pony breeding was still actively carried out were usually under pressure from crofters to demand from the Department the stallion of their choice for service in the following season. Not all of these requests could be met, but in the main the better stallions were allowed to make an adequate contribution in the locality before being moved on. Naturally, they were never allowed to remain in an area

Ponies in leisure moments in Highland settings

longer than three years because of the likelihood that they would be breeding some of their own stock. Inbreeding was not approved of by Highland society.

The number of people who were able to castrate colts was very limited and as a result entire colts were frequently sold as yearlings, together with cattle, at the regular community sales. These colts were subsequently taken to mainland and lowland Scotland for further trading. Even ploughing was done with one horse where two horses ploughed the same land previously. The breed could meet this demand, though it required a great effort from them in many cases. But the total amount of ploughing done became less. As a consequence, less corn was grown and there was less livestock feeding in the winter season. This tended to be a vicious circle with many crofters ending it by deciding to keep a horse no more. But for the quite profitable sales of yearlings, it is doubtful if the horse population of the Highlands would have been maintained, even at a modest level. That there was still considerable Highland pony breeding taking place in the Highlands and Islands in the early part of this century is evident from the statistics relating to the breeding work of the stallions of the Department of Agriculture. Knocknagael Marksman, perhaps the most famous Highland stallion of all, sired 500 foals in his lifetime. He worked as a travelling stallion for many years in the Hebrides before taking up residence in the Department's stud near Inverness where he continued to breed until the year of his death when he was 29 years old. Marksman, as a prolific sire of Highland foals, serves to illustrate the effort that was being made during this time to preserve quality in the breed.

With the emergence of the Victorian era the Highlands acquired a new and quite spectacular popularity. For the first time they received enthusiastic patronage from British royalty. Queen Victoria became enamoured of the Highlands and made visits to various parts whenever she could. Eventually, Balmoral became her Highland home, and it still remains the Highland home of the Royal family. Queen Victoria became familiar with the Highland pony and its merits. She is known to have ridden this animal during her nature trails into regions of the Highlands which had no roads suitable for a carriage. The gentry of England followed her royal example and made a recreational invasion of the Highlands. Grouse shooting on the moors and the stalking of deer in the vast deer forests emerged as new forms of sport for the gentry. Both required the back-up of the Highland pony. Grouse shot in large numbers on the high and remote moorlands required transportation to the shooting lodge. They were carried usually in the wickerwork panniers draped on either side of a garron pony, in the way that peat had been transported across rough Highland ground centuries before. The work of deer stalking was ecologically valuable.

This sport, which represented a substantial Highland industry, would not have been possible without Highland ponies. The garron was well suited to transport the sportsmen—who were not necessarily in good physical condition—to the remote areas of the Highland deer forests. They were also able to transport back to the shooting lodge the deer which had been shot in the mountains. These were mostly stags, very considerable loads of dead weight. Their transportation over many miles of trackless Highland terrain represented demanding work, one that no other type of pony could have performed so well.

That the Highland pony today is of a very high and uniform standard of quality is due largely to the earnest efforts of those who stayed in the business of garron breeding throughout the years when there must have been little or no financial profit in the enterprise. By the middle of the present century the massive conversion of farmwork to tractor power virtually terminated the role of the garron as a worker on the croft. The change was rapid, and for several post-war years the Highlands and Islands were combed by horse dealers buying up garrons at extremely low prices. Few asked these dealers where the horses were destined to go; those who sold them had no further use for them. The animals, through care and selection, had long lifespans and the crofters could no longer afford the considerable cost of maintaining them for long periods when they would be totally unpro-ductive. That many ended in European countries to ease the post-war famine in meat was without doubt. But had this been known, it is questionable if the sale of these animals would have taken place on the scale that it did. The post-war clearance of Highland ponies from crofting communities did not last long, however, for new opportunities to make use of them developed. Not only did the showing of livestock become active, but the new sport of pony trekking became popular in 1953. This new recreational activity heralded the fortunate return of general interest to unspoiled country where only horses could travel easily.

4. Highland Pony Form

The environmental characteristics of the Highlands and Islands of Scotland give the region its own special features created by earthquakes and volcanoes. Ice Ages carved mountains and deep lochs of sea and fresh water, forming glens and massive areas of stone rubble. The dramatic sculpting of the land came to an end with the passing of the last Ice Age when all Scotland settled to the general form it has today. Appropriate adaptations were required of a horse becoming native to this land.

In 1845, Professor David Low of Edinburgh University described Highland ponies as follows:

> Those of the Outer Hebrides are small, round-shouldered, muscular and thickly clad with long hair. Those of the Inner Hebrides are usually of somewhat larger stature. The best of them used to be produced in Mull, Barra, and Islay; and here, tradition refers to changes produced by the horses of the wrecked Armada, a part of which having rounded the Northern Cape, found its way to these dangerous coasts. They are mostly of a brownish-black colour, and some gray. They have the common characters of round shoulders, stout limbs, and short upright pasterns. They are hardy in a high degree, but they have little speed.
>
> The same kind of horses extends to the neighbouring parts of Argyleshire, and, with some change of characters, dependent on the greater elevation and productiveness of the heathy pastures, through all the central and northern Highlands. The prevailing colour is a dull brownish-black. They have abundant hair, stout limbs, and short pasterns. They have good feet, and are sure-footed and hardly in the highest degree. They are well suited for climbing mountains, and manifest great sagacity in making their way through swamps and bogs; but they are lazy and slow, and altogether destitute of the fire and mettle distinctive of the Arabs, the Barbs, and other horses of warmer climates.

The Highland pony, living naturally outdoors throughout the year on the rough terrain of the Highlands where good grazing would exist in isolated portions of land, required to have close forward vision. In the course of his adaptation to his native land by changes taking place in the set of the eyes, the Highland pony has his eyes set over a slightly narrow nose bridge allowing the eyes effective movement further forward and closer than many other breeds. The slightly narrower nose between the eyes in this breed facilitates forward binocular vision better than in some others, and as a result they are able to focus better

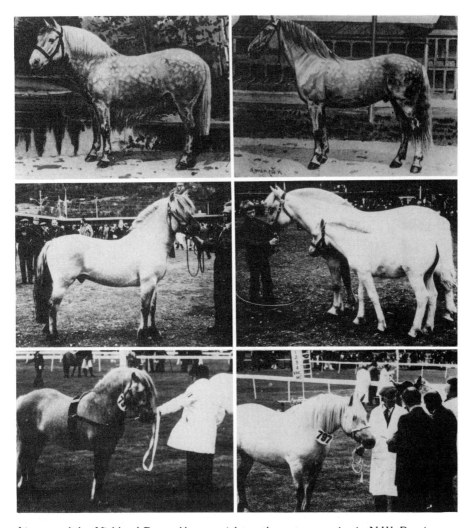

Lineage of the Highland Pony. Above—eighteenth-century ponies in N.W. Russia, middle—Norwegian ponies, bottom—modern Highland Ponies

and react better within their environments. They can also perform certain tasks that require good eyesight, better than other horses might manage. Horses with an adequate degree of frontal vision, in fact, are able to utilize binocular vision, a valuable asset in adaptation. The Highland pony undoubtedly is capable of utilising binocular vision. This is the kind of visual property which gives the animal the ability to focus quickly on objectives directly in front of him. The horse with this capability is obviously at an immediate advantage in dealing with mountainous complicated terrain.

Vision is one of the most important considerations in adaptation. The eyes of the horse are arranged so that it is able to see almost entirely to its rear and completely on both sides all at one time. This spectacular panoramic or scanning capacity of the horse's vision was undoubtedly a key feature in its early adaptation. The range of early forms of predators with which it obviously coped, was considerable. This evolutionary type of adaptation was not without some disadvantage under modern circumstances. Some of the unfortunate consequences of this vital system are the horse's inability to see exactly what he is eating. He is unable to focus his eyes close enough to see objects very keenly if less than four feet from his face. The horse has particular difficulty with visual 'accommodation', that is, in focusing objects directly in front of him. When he concentrates to focus his eyes forward to his maximum ability he appears momentarily to lose the ability to observe consciously to the rear and to the sides.

The advantages of rear vision, in circumstances where the horse was subject to predation, are obvious. Most breeds of horse have their eyes so laterally placed that their rear vision is only blocked by the width of the horse's own body, and even this can be rectified by raising his head high. This vision, together with his keen awareness of sudden movement and his preparedness for quick flight, made the horse, when he was a hunted animal, difficult for potential predators to catch.

Highland ponies at mountain grazing employ frontal vision to a substantial degree. this ability is also of value to those animals on smaller islands which have also acquired the habit of going onto foreshores to forge for seaweeds as a form of foodstuff. The adaptation for forward vision has had its consequences. The principal one is the development of a hair screen over the eyes with the long forelock so typical of this pony. This is essential to deal with wind and driving rain, while continuing to graze.

Another environmental adaptation is the length of mane and the length and density of the hair of the tail. In severe weather when a high wind is blowing the Highland pony, when he ceases to graze, will normally direct the hindquarters into the wind. This allows his tail to be blown between his hind legs while he holds his tail in close to his dock. The tail hair then shields all of that hairless area of his perineum, his inguinal region and the inner thighs. By this means he spares himself the loss of heat and energy reserves essential to take him not only through the winter but also through a spring that can be long and

49

harsh in some years. The combination of cold and wind, especially in wet weather, can inflict great stress upon a horse. Nothing so chills a horse as keen winds with rain or snow. The quantity and quality of hair over the head can both waterproof and watershed, to ensure that ears and eyes are not subject to weathering. The effects of frost in very cold weather can be worse in a saturated horse. This mane, of Highland ponies, with its unique length and density, can act as a waterproof screen for the head, jowls, throat and neck. When left uncombed, numerous long, ropey segments become formed throughout the mane of Highland ponies. Because of the inherent wavy nature of this hair it has the propensity to intertwine and to 'plait' naturally.

Apart from the eyes and ears, the anatomical areas of the head and neck contain vital superficial structures, such as the large, long and superficial jugular veins, and their upper tributaries in the throat and the sensitive tissues and glands in the vicinity of the throat. All require thermal protection.

The density of winter coat and the direction of hair lie, especially over the hindquarters and back, provide an outer periphery to the body which acts as a weather shield, so efficient that ice may form on top of it without transmitting chill to the skin.

The feather, on the fetlocks of the Highlander, is just sufficiently developed to divert and take the run-off of moisture being channelled down the legs to the fetlock points. this saves the hollows and bulbs of the heels—and to some extent the frogs of the hooves—from excessive wetting and its undesirable consequences.

The hirsute nature of forelock, mane and tail in this horse gives it a considerable amount of protection in the summer when the Highlands and Islands are plagued by midges and biting horseflies or clegs. These insects collectively represent an environmental feature so adverse as to reduce habitability in this region when climatic features are otherwise at their most benign. Other forms of livestock and man can sometimes become frenzied by this irritant fly-life but the pony has more tolerance of it. This is due largely to an ability to maintain a defensive fly-screen by continued gentle agitation of its long hair, fore and aft.

Variability of size of this breed has resulted in its being traditionally subdivided by size into a larger 'Mainland' and a smaller 'Western Isles' type. These types in turn are considered to represent the working or draught type and the riding type respectively. This conception is not unreasonable. The Isle of Skye ponies, however, partly by selective breeding and partly by tolerant conditions, are often among the larger specimens, over 14 hands. On the mainland, some Clydesdale influence may have contributed to size in some individuals of half a century and more ago, but the notion of the mainland type as being more suitable for draught work then riding is difficult to prove. Versatility could be the Highland pony's middle name, for it can perform between shafts and under saddle equally well, irrespective of height and coastal classification.

That some insular adaptations have occurred is without question. For example, the Eriskay pony, whilst keeping strength, is recognised as being of fine build. A society now exists to work for the preservation of its type in pure-bred form. The ponies of the Isle of Rhum have been notably insular in their breeding. They also have very recognisable characteristics, the most obvious being growth of hair. Inter-island traffic of horses has long been adequate to create a well-mixed population, one which overlapped with the mainland population. This trafficking has dispersed local adaptations, contributing most of these to the genetic pool of the breed as a whole. The dictates of controlled breeding, whether based on foresight or fashion, wisdom or whim, can still operate, however, to draw selectively from this pool and modify representatives of the breed. Such is the effect of domestication.

The main features of Highland pony conformation are good development of fore quarters, hind quarters and neck, and a compact general appearance. The strength of the fore quarters has been particularly emphasised. Some outstanding specific features of the conformation of the Highland pony include a well-set neck, one which is particularly well developed at the base. The breast also has been described as being typically well developed and wide. The shoulders are described as being well muscled and steep, or oblique, in direction. The hind quarters are visibly muscular and the conformation of the loins is compact. Shortness of cannon bone is a preferred feature. All of these features are developments which have taken place in the breed as a result of its adaptation to its work requirement. Adaptation has also been guided by selection through breeding.

The Highland Pony is now the most versatile and powerful of all the numerous breeds of pony native to Britain. It is indigenous to the Hebrides and the mainland Highlands of Scotland. This hardy horse, of impressive endurance and kindly disposition, is of pony height standing between 13 and 14.2 hands, or up to 145 cms. Grey and dun colours, of attractive shades, are most common. A dark 'eel stripe' usually runs down the back as a significant hallmark.

The Highlander should be screened by a long and thick forelock, which should be long enough to reach well down the face. The head is neat and comparatively small, with a well-shaped, deep and wide forehead. Its eyes are alert and expressive and overlook the concave, slightly dished face. The nose is straight and narrow and its narrow bridge improves frontal vision. Ears are hairy and neat, and the jaws are nicely rounded and strong. The muzzle is large and broad with wide nostrils. The neck is particularly well-developed at the base where it merges nicely with the withers, shoulders and breast. In good specimens, the back and loins are compact, and the tail well set-in.

In this breed, the chest is deep and well sprung. The forelegs are straight and from the front an imaginary line should pass from the shoulder joint straight down through the forearm, the centre of the knee, the length of the cannon bone, the fetlock and the toe of the hoof. A side view of the leg shows the elbows well closed-in and flesh-covered and the leg, to the fetlock, in the true perpendicular. The hind leg permits, when viewed from the side, an imaginary vertical line to pass from the point of the buttock down to the point of the hock and the posterior of the cannon, in the perpendicular. From the rear, an imaginary vertical line passes from the buttock, through the hock and the middle of the fetlock, ending between the bulbs of the heel. The tail should be long and bushy, with wavy hair reaching the vicinity of the fetlocks, and the tail root hair should have good body, especially between the buttocks.

Stallions usually have nine to ten inches of bone; mares have about eight inches. Short cannons and flat bones are good features. Good sloping pasterns, particularly in the forefeet, are desired. Hocks are very well let down, and although hind quarters may be heavy, some are not. Hocks are neat. The feather over the coronets is light and bouncy, and while covering the hoof head adequately, it should not carry far down the hoof. Hooves are rounded and open, more especially the forefeet. The hoof horn is dark, hard and of flinty appearance.

The overall appearance of the pony is one of well-coupled strength, nicely contoured. Beauty of build, of head and expression, is evident. The carriage of the head is upright and alert with large dark eyes. In movement, the horse reaches out well and lifts all its feet cleanly, both in the walk and trot.

The total result of all of these physical features is strength and power, making the animal particularly suitable for endurance riding and draught work. The draught work called for takes various forms. A conventional form is traction of carts, ploughs or other agricultural equipment. Often this has to be done without the assistance of a second horse. Another form of draught which this animal is called upon to provide is porterage. Highlanders originally used the native pony to assist them to carry peat in panniers as well as other items of domestic or personal requirement slung across the back. Its use in deer stalking represents very exacting portering work. Much of its typical work is over ground where there are no roads or tracks, and ground which is beset with obstacles such as rivers, bogs, marsh, rock, and thick heather.

As a consequence of all these requirements, the breed has become physically suited for miscellaneous draught work. The animal has also acquired the physical capacity to utilize leverage, particularly on the fore quarters. Such leverage capacity is essential in assisting the animal to alter its centre of gravity in relation to the dead load whilst it is negotiating difficult terrain. In any horse the neck is the instrument of leverage. Apart from the development of the neck—in particular, development of the neck at its base where it blends in strongly with the shoulder—there is also the development of another physical mechanism to assist leverage. This secondary mechanism is the ratio of forearm to cannon bone, where the forearm is comparatively long and the cannon bone is comparatively short. Such a high ratio of forearm, which is muscular, to cannon, which contains tendons (extensions of muscles), gives an efficient pulley system and allows greater leverage of the limb.

In the course of this type of forced movement of the forelimb, the angles of the shoulder and elbow joints alter very little. During the course of progression of the forelimb, the angle of the shoulder in particular is held fairly constant. The greatest amount of movement that takes place in the bones of the forelimb occurs at the height of the scapula—in the region of the withers—and below the carpus or knee. Since these are the two parts of the forelimb required to alter position most in effecting leverage, we can understand why the musculature relating to these parts has become particularly well developed in this breed.

The musculature involved in flexing the knee and in causing the cannon bone to be used as a lever has well developed muscles which run down the front of the forearm to the knee and down the back of the forearm from beneath the elbow towards the knee joint.

Action of the body in draughtwork, in both of its forms of traction and deadweight carriage, requires strong muscular exertion in the region of the loins and the hind quarters. It should be borne in mind that when being extended to drive the animal forward, even against considerable weight in draughtwork, the thighbone or femur never extends beyond a vertical line from the hip joint to the stifle joint. As with the forelimb, a ratio of gaskin (or second thigh) to hind cannon, in which the latter is of minor length, gives the best coupling arrangement to effect hind limb leverage. For this reason the description of the ideal conformation of the hock of the Highland pony as being 'well set down' is justified. A well set-down hock with adequate musculature in the region of the second thigh gives maximum potential to the limb to extend the leg and improve not only strength of support but leverage.

In order to maintain dead weight over the back, the back itself requires to be comparatively short. For this reason the best conformation for this breed has been described as a back that is short to medium in length. Additional length in the back is likely to contribute to muscular stress in supporting weight. Probably the most critical part of the horse's anatomy in maintaining substantial amounts of weight on its back are the loins. It is essential in this animal, and a fairly constant feature also, that the loins be strong and well coupled.

The slope from the croup to the tail head in this animal is sometimes seen to be comparatively long and steeper than in some other breeds. This is not thought to be an attractive physical feature and for this reason there is sometimes discrimination against it in the show ring. Nevertheless, this type of physical shape of the hind quarters is often found in individual animals which have a particular strength in the hind quarters.

Whilst levering the fore quarters in draughtwork the animal requires to follow through with the forefoot, and this requires a considerable amount of flexion of the fetlock joint. For this reason one looks for a good angle between the cannon bone and the slope from the fetlock to the toe. This angle has been described as one of approximately 135 degrees. Such angulation would allow the forelimb to be carried through in vigorous action and also allow it to be well flexed for its return to a forward position. In the hind limb there is a similar follow-through property in action, and here again the angle between the hind cannon bone and the slope of the pastern to the toe is also well developed; it is normally found in satisfactory conformation to be approximately 145 degrees in angulation.

Yet another feature of conformation which requires to be well developed for traction work is breadth between the shoulder joints. Narrow-chested animals do not have the same traction power as those which are broad in the breast; breast muscles are much better developed and much more prominent in the stronger animal which is capable of impressive traction work. The muscular activity taking place in the fore quarters and limb of the horse during its forward movement is a beautiful piece of mechanism. While the forelimb is moving forward and back the neck and chest muscles are alternatively contracting and relaxing. These are the muscles which form a sling in which the chest hangs between the two shoulder blades. When the leg is moving forward the very long muscle which extends down the side of the neck to the arm contracts and pulls the forelimb forward. The muscles of the breast also pass from the chest to the arm to aid in its leverage. The alternating strong contraction and relaxation of these muscles in pairs is known as reciprocal muscle action. It is this important function of muscles, anywhere in the major muscular parts of the body, which is essential in maximum muscular proficiency. Needless to say, it is this same reciprocal muscle action which, carried out most proficiently, gives the animal not only strength but an even and flowing gait.

The large, nicely rounded and prominent muscle mass about the elbow joint, which is a prominent feature of Highland conformation, represents the triceps muscle. It would appear that one important function of this muscle, which has not always been realized, is that it acts as a shock absorber mechanism to take the impact of the limb upon the ground when considerable weight is put on the forelimb. Most of the body weight of the animal, together with its load, is applied to the foreleg, and such force is resisted by the powerful mass of this triceps muscle.

The dun colour, certainly in the Highland breed, is often associated with a phlegmatic disposition, and this may be the basis of the breed's reputation for good temperament. It is also significant that chestnut is a missing colour in this breed—conspicuous by its absence, in fact. The 'suite of characteristics' of dun colour, eel stripe and sound temperament characterises the breed in a way which is not likely to be coincidental. Here, surely, is an outstanding example of a physical-temperamental relationship. Their deliberate selection is probably due, in large measure, to the wisdom of choice by those breeders who had to live at very close quarters, and in total harmony, with the working ponies they bred. No temperamental chestnut would find favour with them.

Another primitive and occasional feature is the presence of zebra markings, caused by bands of lighter and darker pigmentation. The result can be a patterned effect such as zebra markings on the limbs, lattice markings about the shoulders or forearms, and general brindling. Lattice and zebra markings on upper and lower leg areas respectively can often be seen in old-fashioned, pure-bred Highlanders, and are evidence of primitive ancestry, surely a colour feature worthy of conservation.

In Highland ponies a golden or yellow dun colour was formerly very common. Colours now vary, but are solid. Grey is fairly common in a dappled shade, sometimes with a trace of the dark dorsal stripe. With other colours, such as light-coloured duns, mouse duns, creams and iron-greys, silver traces in the main and tail are not uncommon. Virtually all duns have the dorsal stripe. Other colours include Palomino, black, brown and bay. Black limb points are quite common. The dorsal stripe is almost invariably present in all pure-bred Highlanders, except in blacks, browns, iron-greys and some dark greys. The dun with the dorsal stripe is the primitive colour type. Grey may be considered mutant and has become a popularly selected colour in breeding sires.

In the main, the features which have just been described are those which are characteristically found in the so-called mainland type of Highland pony. They are less obvious in the so-called Western Isles type. The latter is commonly referred to as more suited for riding. Certainly the conformation requirements for riding are somewhat different. There is still of course the need for the strength in porterage to be retained in the conformation of this breed, and for this reason one still looks for strength of loins, strength of hind quarters, an appropriate length of back and again development in the region of the shoulders and neck to permit leverage.

Many of these features of conformation have become more important with the increased popularity of this animal in shows. Most, if not all, of these features of conformation are of functional value to the animal in its natural work and setting, thereby justifying their recognition in the show ring. Its conformation is a testament to its very long history and its adaptation over several millennia to its Highland environment and lifestyle.

The changes of horse usage in the Highlands, brought about by depopulation of crofting communities, the introduction of engine power and the new recreation of nature trailing by pony, have resulted in changed values in conformation of the breed. Phases of cross-breeding, both by historical incident and legislative policy, have also effected minor breed changes. The types most numerous today feature the lighter 'Western Isles' specimens and the larger, heavier 'Mainland' type. 'Garron' was formerly the name, of Gaelic origin, for the gelding of either type. This name is now applied, fondly and respectfully, to all Highland ponies, whether 'cut' or not. It is now a title more than a name.

5. The Clydesdale Invention

Following the tragedy of Culloden, clan power was destroyed and lowland Scotland pursued its own ends as the eighteenth century progressed. Events had moved swiftly after the power loom, invented in England by Cartwright in 1785, had launched the Industrial Revolution. Southern Scottish communities readily accepted this revolution. In the central belt of the country coal was the essence of the new order of things. The coalfields of Lankarshire were particularly convenient and they were explored, charted and gouged for the stuff of industrial power.

Coalmining became a major trade and mining towns and communities rapidly appeared over and across the coal belt. Numerous small towns like Shotts and Forth became miners' dormitories in the county. Larger towns like Wishaw, Motherwell, Airdrie and Coatbridge met the great needs of mining-associated industries. In the county of Lanark coal was essential in the production of power and steel. The heavy industries there needed it as an abundant and convenient supply of good fuel.

This new age called for roads and more roads. The roads needed to be wider, stronger and better surfaced to handle the heavy traffic of pack horses. But delivery by pack horse did not satisfy; not enough coal was conveyed on a single trip from the mines by slow-moving strings of horses carrying the coal in a pair of panniers draped over their backs. Loads on wheels were needed and haulage of cartloads of coal was what resulted. The better the roads, the bigger carts they could support. The heavier the loads to be drawn, the bigger and stronger the horse must be. The taller the horses, the faster they could travel. So the essential link in the chain of production, supply and consumption of industrial power became big, strong, quick horses.

Industrial horses, unlike any before them used for heavy traction, would be working constantly on hard surfaces. They would need good feet—big expansive feet with plenty of gripping surface. They would need a spring in the joints of their limbs, to take the impact of their hard labour on Macadam-surfaced roads. The effort of pulling a three-ton load of coal needed great physical strength in the shoulder and hind

c

quarters. This power needed to be transmitted to strong legs collected closely under the body so as not to dissipate strength sideways and outwards. All this called for unorthodox requirements of limb conformation.

Until then, the heavy horses of the world were usually inclined to bulldog stance. Hind limb hocks closely set together were thought to be an outrageous defect, not likely to be found or favoured. But still, the calculating eye of a good judge of hard-working, heavy horses could see this need in physical construction so as to bring the hind limbs under a big muscular rump and get maximum muscular efficiency and physical durability. The shrewd horsemen of Lanarkshire could grasp the mechanics of the problem very readily. Such big horses were not common, but they existed in Scottish lowland agriculture where they were already appreciated. Some big stallions came on the scene occasionally, but men who had been in Europe could describe the abundance of horses of very great size and bulk which they had seen in the Flemish region of Belgium. Stallions from there would surely be worth breeding from, if they could be brought over from Europe. In the creative heads of Scottish horse breeders, who had strong mares, interest turned to big stallions such as the large, heavy, muscular horses of Belgium. Although they had a common origin in one foundation sire, Belgian horses were differentiated into three types at that time. The most elegant animals were of the Flanders type, but there were also the muscle-bound Brabant and the somewhat smaller Ardennaise. Only the latter two now remain registered by the Belgian breed society—which now recognises the Brabant as the true Belgian.

The Flanders type seems to have gone from its homeland, but it passed into the British horse picture with great effect when it contributed to the Lanarkshire model. Such is the opinion expressed to the author by Professor Vandeplassche in the University of Ghent's Veterinary School, after studying a full collection of early Clydesdale photographs. The old Flanders horses had thick necks but less muscular bulk than other Belgians. They had fine limbs with nicely angulated conformation, short backs and large heads. These were the most valuable Flanders characteristics which went into Lanarkshire, or Clydesdale, in its early horse-producing days. In the county of Lanarkshire, to meet the local demands of industrialisation and more productive farming, specialised breeding of a new, locally-suited type of heavy horse was started by the Paterson family and by the Dukes of Hamilton.

The Hamiltons of Lanarkshire had long been horsebreeders, according to history. The second Lord Hamilton kept a study of horses at Kinneil which was visited by King James IV in 1508. The Dyke, who imported the 'Flemish' horses, though he bore the name of Hamilton, was in reality a Douglas. The date of this influence was towards the end of the seventeenth century, the period of Anne, 'the Good Duchess', who was closely associated with Strathaven. The male line of the Hamiltons had failed, and she was Duchess in her own right. She married William Douglas, a second son of the first Marquess of Douglas, and carried the Duchy of Hamilton into the Douglas family, where it has remained. Her husband, who became Duke by special creation, and she, owing to their Covenanting sympathies, fell out of favour at Court, and lived quietly on their estates. They were among the first to welcome William of Orange, and this association with Holland may have led to the introduction of the Flemish horses. Thus, Clydesdale ancestors came over, in a sense, with William of Orange.

The original infusion of 'Flemish' blood, by the Hamiltons, was reinforced by others from the same source. About the middle of the eighteenth century James, sixth Duke of Hamilton, kept a dark brown Flemish stallion at Strathaven for his tenantry. But the stock which were thus improved were, as described by A.M. Scott, 'the common mares of the country', whose characteristics remained to be developed by careful breeding by the Paterson family. Prior to the Revolution of 1688 there was little selective horse breeding in Scotland. The country had been repeatedly ravaged by war, and raids, and civil factions. It has been well said that the breeders' art is an art of peace. It was evidently true for the Clydesdale horse which was about to emerge.

It is notable that two scholars of the time (who were not horsemen) properly referred to the type of horse in question as 'Flanders', not 'Flemish'. The local history was preserved in an old statistical account by the Rev. David Ure, in a volume on Rutherglen published in 1793, as follows:

> Rutherglen Fairs are famous for the finest draught horses in Europe . . . About a century ago an ancestor of the Duke of Hamilton brought six coach horses from Flanders, and sent them to Strathaven, the Castle being then habitable. They were all handsome black stallions. The surrounding farmers gladly bred from them, and the cross with the Scotch horse procured a breed superior to either, which has been improved by careful breeding. Great attention is paid to colour, softness and hardness of hair, length of body, breast, and shoulders of their

breeders. Every farm almost has four or six mares. The colts are mostly sold at the fairs of Lanark or Carnwath. They excel in the plough, the cart, and the wagon.

The same tradition is referred to by the Rev. William Proudfoot, in his article on Strathaven in the New Statistical Account, written in 1835. He stated that progeny of Flanders horses 'are still to be found here in great perfection and beauty'.

With an inspired choice of a foundation sire, John Paterson had acquired a black 'Flemish' stallion ('Paterson's Black Horse') which was one of the many stud animals of the 'Flemish' breed being imported from the Low Countries during the eighteenth century. As part of the intensive trading taking place between the port of Amsterdam and Britain at this time, many hundreds of breeding horses, of types new to Britain, were introduced and dispersed throughout most parts of England and Scotland.

The early Clydesdales were largely the result of successful blends of local mares, of packhorse type, with the Hamilton 'Flemish'. They were big horses, mostly brown or black in colour with white on the face and legs. These were to be some of the hallmarks of the breed for the next century. Paterson and his stallion got the support of other breeders in the district.

It seems clear that there was a vigorous 'Flemish' shoot grafted on to a native Scottish stock, in the House of Douglas, and that there was also a certain infusion of English blood.

Dimly emerging from the mists of tradition, about the year 1780, appears the figure of 'Blaze', an English stallion imported by one of the Patersons of Lochlyoch. and this horse has sometimes been referred to as the founder of the Clydesdale breed. It would be more accurate to say that succeeding generations of Patersons, with their accumulated experience, and careful selection, were fixing the type, and that 'Blaze' was a powerful instrument in their hands.

'Blaze' was a stylish black horse with good white markings. He might well have been of Flemish breeding by one of the several other stallions of this breed being brought into southern Scotland via England. With another suitable stallion on the scene, a choice could then be made in the breeding of foundation stock for the next generation, and so continuity of the project could be ensured.

Early in the nineteenth century 'the Lampits Mare' is heard of. Lampits Farm is on the banks of Clyde, near Carstairs, where a horse ferry once operated. The origin of the Lampits Mare has not been definitely established, but was traced back to the stables at Lochlyoch. She was purchased at a displenishing sale at Shotts Hill Mill in 1808; the Clarksons of Shotts Hill Mill were related to the Paterson family.

In 'Glancer' we have an ancestor from whom pedigrees can be traced with accuracy. He is said to have been a son of 'the Lampits Mare'. From his loins sprang many famous Clydesdale families including 'Glancer', alias 'Thomson's Black Horse'. He was owned by James Thomson, of Germiston, near Glasgow, and his fees were 'One guinea and a shilling to the groom'.

'Glancer', born in 1810, was the first truly native Clydesdale sire. He sired some good progeny, and from them came his great-grandson 'Champion' in 1821. 'Champion', true to type, was a black horse with white legs. In turn he became the father of 'Clyde', who was the breed's main sire in 1840. From this point on there was a very well-established family tree for the Clydesdale breed. From one Duke of Hamilton with his famous horse 'Prince of Wales' to humbler men with small farms there were dedicated Clydesdale horse breeders ensuring the progress of the breed. The Duke's stallion was one of several 'Princes' breeding in the 1800s. They helped to effect changes in the local horse population. Paterson, who kept breeding records from the start, and gave direction to choice of breeding stock and to the type, deserves the greater credit for the creation of the Clydesdale breed. However, it was not until ninety years after John Paterson's records began that 'Clydesdale' became the accepted breed name. It took a further thirty-seven years for a breed society to be formed.

By 1866 different Clydesdale lines became developed, each with its own minor characteristics while being a good specimen of the breed as a whole. Some lines had stallions of 2,200 pounds weight, of heavy bone, good feet and excellent action, both at the walk and trot. This action was a well-cherished characteristic in the breed from those early days. The 'get' of these lively sires now varied more widely in colour. Black and brown was still most common, but bays, greys, and roans were also appearing. Draughtwork, with big drays and heavy carts, calls for such animals. They worked well on the large farms, on coal tracks and over the improved commercial roads built by Macadam. They filled all manner of needs for powerful animals to draw four-wheeler carts carrying industrial and building materials. The surrounding farmland up around the town of Lanark, away from the industrial areas, was regularly combed for suitable draught horses.

FOOTPRINT

LE CHEVAL DE TRAIT
Ordre des Pachydermes. ...id. ...id
Das Zugpferd

THE BARON

HIAWATHA

Foundation sires of notable type. Note top right—the Flanders horse

Gradually horses were found with some suitable qualities, but large numbers were needed and the search extended throughout Lanarkshire to Carluke, Carstairs, Carnwath, Biggar, Douglas Water, Lesmahagow, Strathaven, Lanark itself and into the shadow of Tinto hill.

Notable horse-breeders were being found further afield than the limits of Lanarkshire—with outstanding sires in Paisley, Kilmarnock, Stranraer in the South-west, and the Mearns in the North-east. This wider circle of breeding allowed some Shire blood from English horses to find its way into the Clydesdale. The Clydesdale in his turn reciprocated and contributed to the Shire type, which was then being developed as the principal heavy horse in England when the Clydesdale Horse Society was being organised in 1877.

The early Scottish breeder paid attention to the subtle angulation of limb joints. Three needs of a mechanical nature had to be met by anatomical features. First, the limbs had to be of strong construction to carry the animal's great weight. Second, they had to be capable of delivering a powerful and steady muscular thrust for draughtwork. Third, the concussion-absorbing mechanisms of the limb had to be particularly well defined in these heavies with their Scottish high-stepping gait.

Much of the arrangement for absorbing concussion in the horse's leg depends on the angulation of its joints at the time of impact, when the hoof strikes the ground. Numerous muscles, tendons and ligments function as springs which absorb and distribute the force of ground contact by permitting flexion of all the upper limb joints and extension of the foot joints. The lower ligaments and tendons possess much elasticity, and the walls and sole of the foot also have some give. The hoof and its anatomical contents absorb a great deal of the initial impact, so the vital design of the expansive hoof of the big horse in Clydesdale allowed the lateral cartilages—close by the heels—to expand. All the soft tissues within the horny chamber of the hoof could be saved shock and counter-shock with wide heels and the cushioning role of the sole's large frog in this type of foot.

The extra blood volume contained within a hoof of efficient oversize has a hydraulic, shock-absorbing effect and helps the hoof to expand with uniformly dispersed pressure. In addition, some of this sudden and increased blood pressure in the hoof drives the slow-moving blood in veins in the lower parts of the limbs back up on its long return journey to the trunk of the body and to the heart. This transmission of shock and pressure up long tubes of venous fluid turns to good use the concussions of long-legged, heavy effort. It is left to the big hock joint of the hind leg to take and absorb much of the stress and strain of impact, leverage and power. Here was the secret of this Lanarkshire horse's special transmission system and wearing power. After a lifetime of hard legwork, this horse, unlike most others, would still have good hocks. They were 'clean' because they were free of lumps, bumps, swellings, protrustions, thickenings and blemishes.

The shape of the hock was so contoured that it did not seem a prominent, protruding joint, in spite of being the largest joint in the entire body. It was a joint with much depth and, although it had considerable size from front to back and width from side to side, it blended so well with the limb above and below that its dimensions were deceptively neat-looking. Perhaps the deep secret was in its special angulation and rotation, the hocks being turned in towards each other at the back; knowledgeable judges always looked quickly to see 'how well the back door was closed'. The secrets of the Clydesdale's legs lay in the science of equine mechanics. In the horse, the action of the hock is linked to the action of the stifle joint above it. Although these joints correspond to the human heel and knee, both joints work in harmony, as the result of a special arrangement in the equine hind leg called 'the reciprocal apparatus'. When either the stifle or the hock flexes or extends, the other joint reciprocates with similar action. The reciprocal apparatus consists of two long muscular bands running down the front and the back of the hind limb. One extends from a point above the stifle to a point below the hock, at the front. The other extends from the back of the thigh bone to the point of the hock joint. Although these bands are muscles, they are composed mostly of tough fibrous tissue and serve largely as pulleys down the front and back of the leg, enclosing both stifle and hock joints in a fibrous parallelogram in which both joints are forced to move in unison because they are tied in to their reciprocal apparatus.

The vital mechanical system of the leg joint is worth a full examination. When the stifle flexes, the hock must flex, and when the stifle extends, the hock extends simultaneously. When the hock is forced by impact to flex, the stifle above must flex to the same degree. But since the stifle is against the belly wall, and virtually covered by the lower flank, its full flexion could be embarrassed or hindered by the abdomen—especially if this is a belly of some capacity. However, when the limbs are shaped with the backs of the hocks in-turned, the stifles above become turned out. Now, in such a horse, when there is reciprocal flexion in the stifle in response to a good springy hock, there is room for the large stiffle joint to yield freely upward and obliquely outward from the belly wall.

This is an anatomical strategy which not only has great capacity for absorbing shock, but also allows the liberal hind leg action, so much a part of gallant equine style. For the hind foot to be plucked up with high action at each step, the hock is required to flex sharply and the stifle, in turn, is obliged to flex in the same fashion and to the same degree. It follows that if the stifle is to do this well, it needs to be able to move easily forward and upward. It does this best if it is directed very slightly outward from the flank.

A further benefit of the reciprocal apparatus to any heavy horse is the ability of this mechanism to become fixed when the stifle is held extended. If the stifle joint is tightly held in extension the hock is effortlessly fixed; the hind legs are then secured to support the posterior weight of the stationary horse with little effort.

Further down the leg there is an associated assembly of flexible, fibrous, elastic ligaments which support the fetlock and the other foot joints. This supportive apparatus of the foot allows the fetlock to 'stay', or remain bent, without the foot becoming overextended, or over-stretched, as it takes weight. The 'stay apparatus' goes down into the hoof and is present on both fore and hind feet.

Although the fore leg does not have the reciprocal apparatus—so invaluable to the hind leg in sustaining weight in the stationary stance—it does have its own equivalent. This is the 'check apparatus' which also helps to support the fetlock joint and permit the fore legs to be maintained in the standing position with little effort. This check apparatus is a fairly elaborate assembly of long tendons. These variously begin above the shoulder joint, in front of the elbow, and at points above and below the back of the knee, terminating by attach-ment to the bones of the foot.

Economical strain-free standing was important to a horse of much weight and with such angulation featured in its leg joints as was the Clydesdale. This was derived from the strength of its check apparatus of the fore leg, the reciprocal apparatus of the hind leg and the stay apparatus in both fore and hind feet. Although all horses have the same equipment, the unique size of the Clydesdale hoof allowed nature to enhance its function by permitting the critical internal attachments of supportive apparatus to be large, strong and reliable in the role of independent suspension.

As the work horse drives his hoof down at each heavy step, a shock runs up the leg. These upward forces tend to close the elbow joint in front and the stifle joint behind. Nature made provision for these factors, but careful selection by Clydesdale breeders helped nature in providing good shock-absorbing muscles. The impact of great weight on the foreleg, acting particularly on the already-bent elbow joint, is taken up by the triceps muscle. This complex muscle connects the shoulder region to the point of the elbow and constitutes the large muscular mass which visibly fills out the area over the elbow. While standing, the triceps is relexed and its soft bulge is then most noticeable. It is at the moment of impact that this muscle must do its work, by contracting quickly and absorbing shock.

The shock-absorbing muscle for the hind limb is the *quadriceps*. This four-headed muscle comes down from the region of the hip joint and has a single fixture below on the knee-cap, or patella, of the stifle

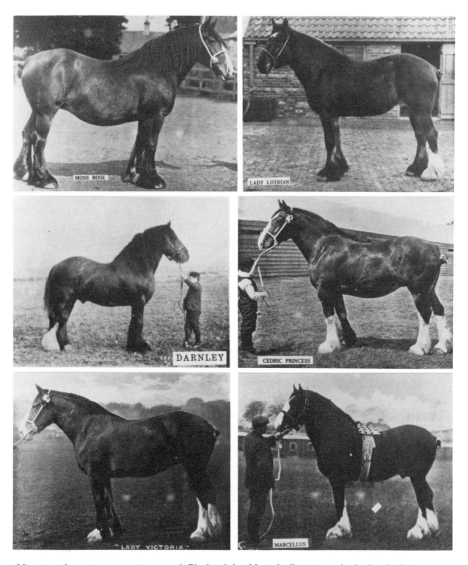

MOSS ROSE

LADY LOTHIAN

DARNLEY

CEDRIC PRINCESS

"LADY VICTORIA"

MARCELLUS

Nineteenth-century specimens of Clydesdale. Note bulk, strength, lack of white.

joint where the hind leg merges into the flank. It constitutes the large muscular mass over the outside face of the upper thigh. Somewhat like its counterpart, the triceps of the foreleg, this muscle is relaxed and inclined to bulge above the joint below with the horse stationary, since it does its critical work by contracting only at the moment of impact of the hind foot on the ground. The hind legs also need *adductor* muscles and these create the bulges of the inner thighs. These extra shock-absorbers are vital to the horse in the business of heavy labour, in the forms of weight-bearing or traction. In cart work the shafts transmit much of the vehicle's laden weight over the animal's back via the saddle carrying the chain which links the shafts to each other. But the equally demanding work of traction calls for good muscular development.

As the forelimb takes most of the responsibility of carrying weight, so the hind limb takes most of the responsibility of pushing. In traction work the hind limbs are forced backwards by the contraction of muscles in the rump. The great muscle mass of the hindquarters largely consists of the *gluteal* muscles which give the haunch its rounded contours. The posterior curvature of the rump's shape, however, is due to muscles which are critically important in pushing the body forward. These correspond to the hamstring down the back of the human thigh. When well developed in a good work horse, this 'hamstring' muscle group stands out quite prominently as a long, thick, curved band running from the point of the buttock down to the lower thigh.

In general appearance, it has been said of the Clydesdale that it 'stands over more ground' than any other breed of horse. Apart from its total impression of massiveness, its chief characteristic is a blend of power and refinement. The Clydesdale possesses finely sculptured weight without displaying bulk or grossness in any form, making it a finely built heavyweight. The horse is marked with great appeal by extensive white over the face and white legs of flowing hair of fine quality. The abundance of hair draping the fetlock and hoof creates an attractive bell-bottomed effect. The silken hair runs down the back of the leg and just touches the ground behind the heels. This 'feathering' of the leg is completed by the full bouncy hair, bobbing round the hoof head. All this hair covers most of the foot, exaggerating the good-looking legginess of the Clydesdale's general and basic appearance.

In action, the Clydesdale flounces into its own with an unmatched style. Showing long springy strides with high lift of the knees and hocks in all gaits, this horse has its own impressive and captivating aura. Watching the horse's 'way-of-going' from behind, the shoe is fully shown—so complete and supple is the pluck of each foot in every stride in straight and true steps. The moving Clydesdale advertises his symmetry, activity, strength and endurance with an obvious appetite for work. No other working horse could be so huge, stylish, perky and colourful.

In colour this breed has much splendour, though the reddish chestnut colour is a notable omission. This might reflect on some slight prejudice in Scotland against chestnut horses, which do sometimes have unwelcome and unpredictable volatility. In the Scottish heart there is a special place for canniness, even dourness, but there is less regard for volatility—at least in livestock. Clydesdale colours are commonly brown, bay (light brown body with black mane and tail) and roan. The roans are particularly attractive, though they were not popular with the early breeders. In Clydesdale roans the prevailing coat colours tend to be rust brown or black, and this is thickly interspersed with white hairs. The roan effect may be over the whole body, either evenly or in a speckled pattern. Often the roan colouring is in large patches, on the shoulders and the flanks particularly. Some shades of roan, such as strawberry roans and blue roans, are very beautiful; these shades have basic colours of light brown or black respectively. Black and pure grey Clydesdales are not now common, though they were frequently seen on the streets of Glasgow within living memory. Splashings of white are common in this breed and there is usually much white on the face and legs. The shanks and their feathers are usually white. Sometimes the white colour on the limbs extends onto adjacent parts of the body. No other work horse is so generously endowed with dazzling white decorative hair. This is quite appropriate to the controlled gaiety of temperament characteristic of this classical animal. In addition to the impression it gives of good humour, the Clydesdale has an exceptionally quiet disposition. For its size, weight and lively power it is remarkably easy to control and to 'break', or train to work in any harnessing.

In the natural Clydesdale stance the forelegs are held well under the shoulders and the hindlegs well under the quarters. In other words, the limbs are closely coupled to the body which is an excellent design of engineered horse flesh for maximum power. Although the forelegs are very straight, the hocks of the hind limbs are turned slightly inwards, towards each other. This is a most unusual characteristic, deemed undesirable in any other breed, but it is one which affords greater leverage potential, greater drive and purchase, at the hind end. The slope from the front of the fetlock to the 'toe' of the hoof is long and well-angled to a straight line. As a result of a very long sloping pastern, on the forefeet particularly, the spring in the step is assured.

The limb bones are noticeable and noteworthy; they are clean and flatter than in any other horse and give that special dense and 'flinty' character. In every respect, the Clydesdale's limbs are truly splendid natural structures; the hoof in particular is superbly designed. The very large hooves are wide and well-rounded in front. The heels are open at the back. All of the hoof-head is quite prominent, with widely extended springy rims. With such feet the horse is singularly well equipped, among heavy horses, for wear and tear on all kinds of surface. The big hoof spreads out impact forces. The wide heels allow expansion and contraction with each step, and this 'give', in addition to absorbing shock, aids the circulation of the lower leg. The open hoof heads allow the inner bones of the foot room to yield to pressure. This reduces the tendency to extra calcification which endless hammering on hard surfaces encourages. Even small calcifications on critical sites cause permanent lameness (and the consequent loss of a useful horse). This horse is by no means immune to such developments but it has much natural insurance against them.

The Clydesdale's head shows frankness, intelligence and capability. There is a broad, open forehead, a nice breadth between bright, clear and intelligent eyes. One horse expert, with a lifetime's experience, said that if he had only one feature of a horse available for his inspection to decide on its purchase—he would nominate its eyes. The Clydesdale would please him well. The ears are large and attentively flared a little. The face is noble and manifestly handsome with a lean profile of straight outlines which gently change to curves towards the nose and muzzle. The muzzle itself is expansive, and includes the large nostrils which contribute to an aristocratic expression. By their location close the upper lip, the soft-edged and widely dilatable nostrils lengthen the clean profile of the nose, giving facial dignity. In both sexes, the upper lip often sports a large and wavy moustache, the two sides of which are separated in the middle; these grow across the lip to be finished off with neat upward points. Such an adornment would be the delight of an old-time sergeant major. For that matter, it probably once did inspire many men to cultivate a facsimile.

The Clydesdale does not have the heavy lower jaw and prominent jowl of most large horses, but has a strong, long lower jaw without any heaviness of jowl. The jawbone extends, with clean lines, from the throat region to the lower lip and a generously soft chin, which overfills the cupped hand when fondled. The line of mouth is long and straight. Its length suggests a slight smile which is not an incongruous

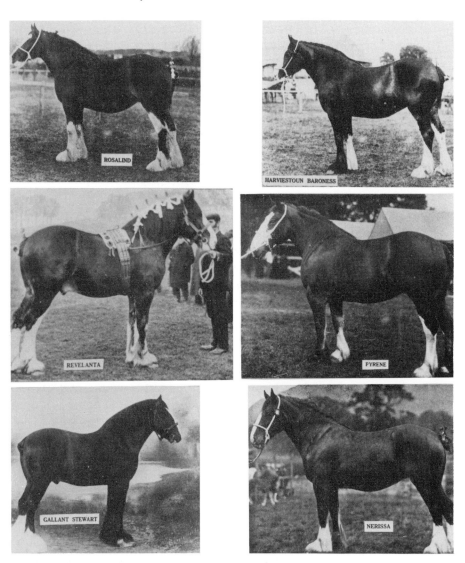

Specimens of Clydesdale at the turn of the century. Note white on legs and faces, height

expression on a head which presents, overall, a picture of equine serenity.

The neck is yet another special feature. From a shoulder, so nicely sloped and blended into this whole area of the forequarters as to be aerodynamic in shape, the extended, strong neck rises with a notable curving topline of long crest. The sides of the neck are flat expanses of strongly muscled substance, with expansion to a deep base where neck becomes shoulder. The hair of the forelock and mane is fine of texture but dense and long enough to sweep down, partly over the face and neck. The neck's crest joins the withers, which are high. This is an anatomical necessity for bearing weight. The convex curve of the crest changes nicely to a shallow concavity of the short back. This part of the top line of the horse gently changes again to the rounded-off line of the hindquarters. Beneath all this curvaciousness is a strong barrel-chested trunk and an abdomen of plenty.

The quarters, packed with power, are long and blend nicely with the thigh. The thigh too is long, favourably endowed with muscle and sinew and coming well down to the hocks. As the forelegs had their broad flat-fronted knees, so the limb behind features broad, long, clean-lined and shapely hocks. But whereas the forelegs are very straight from beneath the shoulder to the flexure of the fetlocks without any knock-kneed suggestion, the slightly inturned hocks bring the points of the hocks quite close together. The shanks of the hind legs are therefore seen close together too, when viewed from behind. This gives the animal a genuine suggestion of being very strong 'sprung' in his hocks. Even in a static stance, with his fore feet planted closely together and his hind similarly close, the Clydesdale always looks ready to move on, promptly with ample power.

The physical needs of a horse of power are both general and specific. A big and strong bony frame is an obvious need. The horse's skeleton, or 'bone', can be adjudged by encircling the foreleg immediately below the knee with one's hand. As this measure increases from ten inches to eleven, twelve and more, so a greater size of skeleton is determined. The knee itself tells much about the skeletal type of the animal. Knees that are broad and flat in front are good evidence of dense or 'flinty' bone. Such bone formation is the type needed by the working horse. The immense stresses and strains which the equine muscular system can generate at work may create small outcrops of secondary bone at vulnerable places on the limbs and back. These lead to sundry infirmities which progressively interfere with the full use of a horse. A rounded front to the knee is indicative of a lighter and more supple frame, such as is seen in the Arab horse.

The practised eye, in judging the potential of a work horse, focuses on the limbs, their joints and the knees in particular both standing and running. Hugh MacDiarmid noted this among horses at a fair, in these lines:

> Brood mares of marvellous approach, and geldings
> With sharp and flinty bones and silken hair.

Another general need is a sizeable chest, for the heart and lungs of a horse are dependent on each other, as they truly determine horse-power. These organs need size and space for optimum function. A trunk which is well rounded out to the elbows has lung capacity; one which has a flat inward slope of the ribs, giving much space between the elbow and chest, does not promise good oxygenation and inherent staying power. The general muscling of a strong horse is prominent both fore and aft. A comment of a keen Clydesdale judge is well and fondly remembered—'He's no a horse for me if he hasnae got a big round erse'.

But it is in some specific sets of muscles that the key to great strength lies. Consider awhile the most basic mechanical demand on a heavy horse—the support of his own body. The forelimbs of the horse unladen support 60% of his total weight. In the case of the Clydesdale at the trot, over half a ton is repeatedly placed on each forefoot with every step. Unlike the hind limb, there is no bone connection between the upper foreleg and the central skeletal frame; the chest is supported by a muscular sling which is a large fan-shaped muscle situated on the side of the neck and chest called the *serratus* muscle. It is split into two parts: one part has the wide end of the fan fixed to the last five bones of the neck and it converges to a point of fixation on the under surface of the shoulder blade at its topmost anterior edge. The other part of the muscular sling has its fan-shaped serrated edge fixed to the lower parts of the first nine ribs, and its pointed end also is inserted on the under surface of the shoulder blade at its topmost posterior edge. The serratus muscles on either side of the trunk therefore form an elastic support which suspends the trunk between the shoulder blades, slightly below the withers. Contracting together, these muscles raise the chest; contracting singly, on one side, the weight is shifted to the limb on the side of the muscle acting.

With the weight of the trunk being transmitted to the inner side of the shoulder blade on each side there is a tendency for the upper edges of the blades to be pulled inwards. This causes the lower part of the limb to be subjected to an outward sideways force. To check this is the function of a group of well-developed muscles—the *pectorals*.

These form a large fleshy mass of breast which occupies the space between the front of the chest and the shoulders. The action of these pectoral muscles is mainly to draw the limbs together and thereby counteract the tendency of sheer body weight to cause the fore limbs to do 'the splits'. The rhythmical contractions of these muscles also give walking power. When these muscles are well developed they are distinctly visible on the animal as the rounded and prominent breast muscles. It will be appreciated that their volume contributes to the width of the breast, or brisket, in front and that the broad-chested horse is built for power, as observed by Burns in this line concerning the Auld Farmer's mare Maggie:

> An spread abreed thy weel-filled brisket
> Wi' pith an' power.

The breast muscles give the animal breadth of shoulder to fill a collar. They also need to be well developed, of course, to support the massive chest. Few horses in the world ever had such girths before the Clydesdale. These breast muscles serve another important function for a year-round worker in northern climes. The breast muscles, or pectorals, of the horse contain some white muscle fibres, and when this special muscle tissue shivers it quickly liberates extra energy to boost body heat. The larger this muscle, the more the thermal reserve. Doubtless big breast muscles served the horse well in cold stables and fields during bitter spells of winter in north-eastern Scotland, where they found so much favour as the breed developed.

From the earliest days in the establishment of the breed as the standard work horse in Scotland the Clydesdale was appreciatively adopted on north-eastern farms, where so much of the country's ploughing was done. Lanark itself has plenty of cold, keen wintry winds. Farms in upper parts of the country, which are often close to a thousand feet above sea level, are without a significant natural barrier to the ripping, southwesterly, cold, wet wind which prevails there.

It is not a low temperature by itself that chills a horse, for horses can live outdoors at very cold temperatures without too much difficulty, if they have shelter from wind. They are in difficulty, however, if they have to deal with strong, cold winds over forty kilometers per hour. If they are wet also, the problem can be compounded to a health crisis. Upper Lanarkshire was a good nursery for a breed of horse that could work through the 'back end' of autumn and see out the winter.

The heavy use of horses in the main towns and cities meant a large

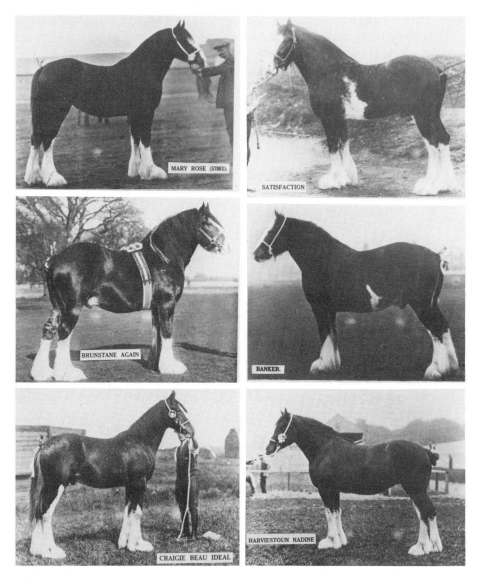

Clydesdale specimens in the 1920s, the heyday of the breed. Note colour, long clean limbs, long white hair (feathering) of lower parts of legs, elegant appearance

and constant demand for young horses. Breeding Clydesdales became an important industry. To help with this breeding, in many farming areas of the country the Scottish system of hiring stallions was begun. This system of district-hiring stallions did more than anything else to disseminate good sires and to fix the best breed characteristics. Many district societies held stallion shows within their own area prior to 1870, and complete records of hiring go back to 1837. A stallion show was in existence in the old Glasgow Cattle Market for several years prior to 1844, when the great foundation sire 'Clyde' won first prize.

At local shows stallions competed for a premium—usually fifty pounds. The owner of the winning horse was then under an obligation to 'travel' his stallion in the breeding season in the area covered by the society and at terms which were specified in the premium contract. Local district shows were eventually abandoned and it was arranged to hold one great Spring Show and Hiring Fair at Glasgow each February, under the auspices of the Clydesdale Horse Society, headquartered at 93 Hope Street in Glasgow. This arrangement gave a great impetus to the hiring system. In time the system became so popular that horses were booked for hiring up to three years ahead. The cash premium for winning stallions then increased to a hundred pounds.

Through the medium of hiring, Clydesdale stallions were drafted into service in Galloway, Kintyre, Midlothian, Bute, Renfrewshire, Ayrshire, Lanarkshire and Aberdeenshire, as well as the northern counties and midlands of England. At annual fairs and auction sales held at centres in both the North of England and the North-East of Scotland, thousands of the best type of heavy draught geldings changed hands.

Horses were important to Glasgow's building rush to house the new population which had tripled in the first half of the nineteenth century to a third of a million inhabitants. The entire Clyde valley was inundated by thousands of uprooted Highlanders, added to whom were the vast numbers of Irish immigrants driven from their homes by the potato famine of 1840. The great range of heavy industries required a hugh labour force of workers and an equivalent force of working horses of a uniform type to perform standard tasks. So the time was ripe for the adoption of this new and special breed of heavy work horse. The livestock breeders of Lowland Scotland were equal to the situation and gave, just not a suitable industrial horse, but a breed pre-eminent in the entire world. Wherever the heavy horse was needed, there was the Clydesdale with strength and style, with refined beauty and power.

The foremost stallions and mares were now being prominently

shown at the annual Royal Highland Show and they were of very wide appeal from their displays there. Foreign approval of this breed was fulsome. Its basic characteristics, including height and weight, were now well established and the breed in general was recognised as having good temper, nicely feathered limbs, large feet, fine white shanks, nicely sprung pasterns and an attractive head. Good specimens acquired great value. Working Clydesdales would be purchased with great care at any of the horse shows and sales which were a regular feature in various parts of the Central and North-east Lowlands of Scotland. Towards the end of the nineteenth century a good Clydesdale could fetch £100 in such a market. At that time this represented twice the wage for a year's work by a horseman. 'Baron's Pride', born in 1890, was then considered to be the best of his breed to that date. He had one outstanding son, 'Baron of Buchlyvie', or 'The Baron', born in 1900 and bred by William McKeich of Woodend Farm, Buchlyvie. The brown foal developed a very fine build and was engagingly marked with a white face and three white shanks. He grew to weigh one ton when mature. This horse's general contribution to the breed cannot be overstated, but his singular contribution was probably through his son 'Dunure Footprint'.

Born in his Ayrshire home in 1908, 'Footprint' sired about 5,000 foals in his life—all by natural breeding. The stallion died aged 22 years. At the height of his breeding powers he could serve, at £60 a time, a new mare every two hours throughout the day and night in the middle of the breeding season. His groom kept him in condition, it is said, with frequent drinks of beaten raw eggs and gallons of milk. By the end of his peak breeding season, however, he was falling off his mares after serving them. Such was the breeding value of this horse that his owner, William Dunlop, allegedly refused £30,000 for him 1919 (the equivalent of about a million today). 'Dunure Footprint' remains the most famous Clydesdale of all time, not only for his breeding powers, but also for his physical merit; he was thought by many to be better than his own father, 'The Baron of Buchlyvie'. 'Footprint's' sons and daughters won virtually all the show prizes in the country for thirteen years after his death. His sons won major awards every year between the two world wars. He was the greatest sire the breed knew, although there were hundreds of other licensed Clydesdale stallions throughout Scotland in his lifetime.

Among breeders, there is little doubt that James Kilpatrick of Craigie Mains became the leading figure. He won more of the

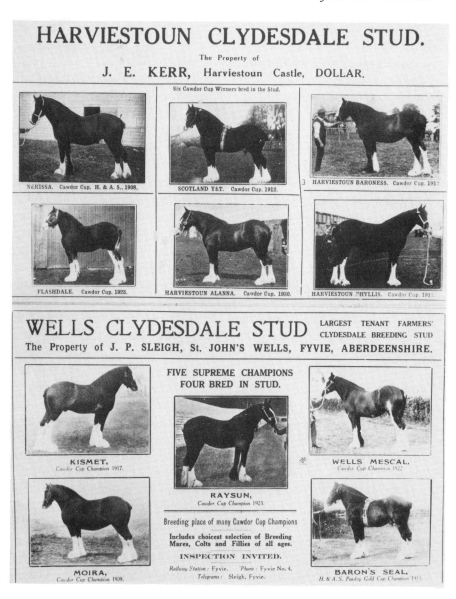

HARVIESTOUN CLYDESDALE STUD.

The Property of

J. E. KERR, Harviestoun Castle, DOLLAR.

Six Cawdor Cup Winners bred in the Stud.

NERISSA. Cawdor Cup, H. & A. S., 1908.

SCOTLAND Y&T. Cawdor Cup, 1912.

HARVIESTOUN BARONESS. Cawdor Cup, 1912

FLASHDALE. Cawdor Cup, 1923.

HARVIESTOUN ALANNA. Cawdor Cup, 1930.

HARVIESTOUN PHYLLIS. Cawdor Cup, 1915

WELLS CLYDESDALE STUD
LARGEST TENANT FARMERS' CLYDESDALE BREEDING STUD

The Property of J. P. SLEIGH, St. JOHN'S WELLS, FYVIE, ABERDEENSHIRE.

KISMET,
Cawdor Cup Champion 1917.

FIVE SUPREME CHAMPIONS
FOUR BRED IN STUD.

WELLS MESCAL,
Cawdor Cup Champion 1922

RAYSUN,
Cawdor Cup Champion 1923.

Breeding place of many Cawdor Cup Champions

Includes choicest selection of Breeding Mares, Colts and Fillies of all ages.

INSPECTION INVITED.

MOIRA,
Cawdor Cup Champion 1909.

Railway Station : Fyvie.   'Phone : Fyvie No. 4.
Telegrams : Sleigh, Fyvie.

BARON'S SEAL,
H. & A. S. Paisley Gold Cup Champion 1915.

The array of select breeders at two famous Clydesdale breeding farms

important Clydesdale trophies than any other breeder has done. At the annual Glasgow Stallion Show and the Royal Highland Show Kilpatrick had his own era as a winner. He saw the Clydesdale become virtually the only heavy breed of horse in Scotland. Acceptance of this, their native breed of work horse, by Scotland's horsemen, was so complete that by 1924 the Clydesdale was the only heavy breed of horse with stallions licensed in Scotland.

From its beginning the Clydesdale was a classical 'cold-blooded' strain of horse. It was therefore an end product in Scotland of the prehistoric coarse-legged, thick-bodied, large-headed horse depicted in French cave drawings. This primitive horse apparently reached the western coast of the Continent of Europe after a migratory trek of centuries from Central Russia. In the Low Countries it duly gave rise to cold-blooded strains whose characteristic head was large with expansive nasal passages and sinus cavities—anatomical features considered helpful to survival in cold. These large warming chambers of the head created a heavy nose and an upper respiratory route which would warm cold air as it was breathed in, to pre-heat it before it reached the lungs. Cold air was therefore not so likely to chill and stress the inner tissues of the animal's chest. This allowed the temperature of the body's core to be maintained more safely in freezing conditions. The Roman nose of many a plain, ordinary Clydesdale was undoubtedly a legacy from an ancestral link with the Ice Age.

The large cold-blooded horse was the Great Horse of the Middle Ages which was used as the war horse of the Crusaders. All experts agree that the large draught breeds are all descended from this European Great Horse. Evidently the Clydesdale acquired many war-horse genes—such as its potential for vigorous dash—through its Crusader connection.

Recently, fresh archaeological accounts and some older historical Flemish literature have been translated from the French into English by Dr. Yves LeGal of Memorial University, Canada, who summarizes this study in a private report. In general it reinforces the traditional view about the Clydesdale's continental ancestry but confirms that the terms 'Flanders' and 'Flemish' were carelessly and synonymously used in describing early Belgian horses and, in particular, the breed type of the Low-County stallion which was used as the foundation sire of the Clydesdale. LeGal's translation follows and shows that it was Flanders blood, not Flemish, which went into the Clydesdale:

> The evidence of the existence of pre-historic horses in Belgium is the result of excavation of caverns in the Lasse Valley by E. Dupont in charge of the paleontologic exploration of the caverns from the Meuse Valley and from its river on the Belgian territory.

From the conformation, dimensions and characteristics of several pieces of skeleton found in this cavern it is assumed that horses with large skeletons were present during that period. These strong horses were the origin of the Flanders-Flemish-Barbancon evolution.

The evolution of the Belgian horse across the centuries has been conditioned by war requirements. In his commentary on the Gallic War, Julius Caesar reported that the Belgium nation was by far the most powerful due to its cavalry. In 57 B.C. Caesar stated that 'the cavalry of Trevires was the most powerful ever in the world'.

On several occasions the strategic needs have modified the type of Belgian, its size and its gait. During the middle ages the bataille horse was represented by a large-size animal, quite slender with a strong skeleton, powerful muscles and large and solid articulations. In addition to his power, this horse was extremely courageous and endowed with a Greek agility. It was a powerful war horse when charging.

During the middle ages the large Belgian horse was used for the battle-field or for farming. The war horse was of the same type as the farming horse, but the discovery of gun powder during the Renaissance, brought profound divergence between the war and farm horse. The first had to be a pure breed and many breeding studs were created for this horse. Several breeding centres remained completely free from cross-breeding and were preserves of Belgian horses. The last breeding stud, at Gembloux, was closed in 1864. Thereafter, only brabancon and condruzien stallions remained for the improvement of the breed.

Before the standardization of the Belgian breeds several *varieties* peculiar to each agricultural region could be found. Among the most important varieties were the Ardennaise, the Brabant and Flanders. With the occupation of Polders, a special variety—the Flemish horse—was formed in the 19th century. The former Flemish horse has now gone. Since 1885, it has been replaced by the Belgian Brabant.

In the history of the Belgian horse, it is important to make the distinction between the Flanders and the Flemish. According to Meuleman the horse from Flanders is of Belgian origin. The Flanders horse used to occupy the sandy regions of Flanders and was derived from the horse found in the centre of the country. The Flemish horse is the Flanders horse produced in some restricted region of the Polders and transformed by the many environmental conditions found in this low and damp region.

The Flanders horse was an equine celebrity resulting from Belgian breeding. It was in Flanders that the middle-ages knights bought the horses which were able to carry weight, not only with elegance, but also without fatigue. The Flanders horse was often portrayed alone on paintings done during the middle ages period. It was then the tallest, the heaviest and the strongest horse of war. After the Gravelines and St. Quentin's victories, the Flanders horse was not to be found any more on the battle field. He was then used for slow labour in the farm and in industry. The Flanders horse was imported on several occasions in the United Kingdom where he gave birth to the Clydesdale.

The Flanders horse was stocky, heavy, tall. His height varied between 1.6m to 1.75m, reaching, in some exceptions, to 1.8m. It did not have the same stocky stature and cubic conformation which are the essential qualities of the actual Brabancon. Its coat was dark, or black, or beige, or chestnut but generally whole-coloured. The head was large, fairly long, the forehead abrupt, shoulders strong but short, the buttocks high and muscular, the hips were very wide, the chest fairly low but not as bent as in the Brabancons and the flanks were exceedingly long. The limbs were long, very lean and slim with quick articulation. The fetlock joints were round and hooves large and flat.

This latter general description brings out Clydesdale characteristics. The final point about the hoof of the Flanders horse, so very characteristic of the Clydesdale, makes it clear that the Black Horse used by Paterson, and probably the others used by the Hamiltons, as the foundation of the Clydesdale breed were wrongly identified. Paterson's horse was of the Flanders breed since the Flemish variety only became formed after Paterson used his horse. The record on this requires correction, since although it was corrected in 1793 by the Reverend Ure, the error has been perpetuated until recent times.

In retrospect it is obvious that the most influential factors in the organized development of the Clydesdale horse were the publication of the Stud Book and the Scottish system of stallion hiring. In addition, due acknowledgement must be given to the inherent merits of Lanarkshire mares, which were bred to the imported stallions of the Hamiltons. They must have had many local adaptations and no doubt had many varied qualities of suitability for Scottish farming as Flanders breeding was being added. The native, unrefined, farm horse of Central Lowland Scotland undoubtedly possessed the outline for a Clydesdale breed, awaiting the extra feature to be written in cold blood for the completion of a great living invention of Nature and of Man.

6. The Ploughing Trade

By the middle of the nineteenth century Scotland was well established as a hale and hearty nation, having restored itself as a power in the world. Over the preceding century, its turbulent history had faded into the past. The main activity of the nation was changing from agricultural work to heavy industry. The latter supported a larger population which had gravitated into the cities and towns in the central lowland belt of Scotland. But in the north-east of the country in the area inland from Aberdeen, a broad fertile and highly productive agricultural region also had an increasing population. Much of this rural population was involved in more intensive farming methods than had been employed in the past.

Scotland's agriculture in general, although it was now secondary to the industrial interests, had emerged by this period into tillage on a grand scale. Few agricultural lands were not put to the plough. Ploughing, of course, was done by pairs of heavy horses, with each plough being handled by a single man looking after the team. These ploughmen became the important artisans of agriculture but their importance was not reflected in the conditions under which they worked. Mostly they worked on 'farmtouns' which were extensive farms, dotted throughout the lowland regions extending up into the north-east and which employed substantial numbers of 'farm servants'. These farms, though privately operated and sometimes privately owned, required specially skilled people dwelling on the farm on a hired arrangement. There would be milkmaids and dairy men to look after the cattle, odd-job men or orramen, the grieve who acted as foreman and there would be the horsemen.

Horsemen were principally involved with ploughing and harrowing the land, but apart from this work of tillage they were also involved in the perennial work of carting crops in from the fields, crops such as potatoes, turnips, hay, corn and barley. Their work was varied and clearly was of great importance to the success of the farmtoun's annual output. Nevertheless the ploughmen were normally housed under very primitive conditions, usually in bothies. They were fed reasonably well but there was little variety or attraction in the food provided. The average farmtoun throughout Scotland had about three or four ploughmen, but larger numbers of horsemen were employed on estates. These men, living in bachelor quarters, sometimes very crowded, were obliged to make their own entertainment at night at the end of the day's hard work. Much of their entertainment was in the form of inventing and singing bothy ballads. David Kerr Cameron has recorded a detailed account of the nature of life and work of these men in his classic book *The Ballad and the Plough*.

Many people can still remember the tail end of that era when 'bothymen' seemed to be a race of their own. They were often dour by nature, often eccentric in some of their ways and often droll with a dry sense of humour. Their main pleasure was in performing their work on the farm with as much skill as possible, and beyond that their pleasures were essentially simple. It was typical for a ploughman to be hired to work on a farmtoun for a single season. At the end of this time he might wish to move on, or he might be required to leave. So it was that these ploughmen found themselves shifting around the countryside moving from farm to farm, season by season. This was the problem of working life which faced them when they wished, in the course of time, to become married and to acquire some more settled type of life. To enter marriage, unless they were well-established in a farmtoun, they were often obliged also to give up the trade of ploughing, a trade demanding great skill, strength and ingrained knowledge.

The wide range of techniques necessary to perform their work all year round was very considerable and their skills could not be acquired from books or through training schools of any kind. They learned the hard way—on the field under the critical eyes of others more experienced. If they became men of considerable experience they were sometimes given the opportunity to occupy a cottage on the farm. This would allow them to take a wife and raise a family and have some degree of stability in their domestic lives. Yet there was always the threat that at the end of the season their services would no longer be needed or desired—then there would be an automatic eviction from the tied cottage, home of the ploughman, his wife and family.

Even those who acquired the best conditions and the most recognition in the ploughing trade still found that they were engaged in an uncertain occupation. If illness befell them there was very little respite they could take from their labours without their infirmity catching the attention of the farmer, who in most circumstances, would then recognize that the ploughman had come to the end of his useful term.

Before first light at dawn the dairy staff would be up and about to milk and feed their cattle. The horsemen would be allowed to sleep a little longer, being excused these dairy chores. Their first job in the day was to feed and groom their horses. But the stable was a warm place which the horses, with the heat of their breath and their bodies, had warmed during the night. The warm stable was a good place to start the day. When grooming was finished it would be breakfast time.

Breakfast was, by tradition, either brose or porridge. Brose was simple to make but very nutritious; in spite of its monotony for breakfast every morning in life it was generally enjoyed. Brose was made by mixing a few handfuls of oatmeal with half a teaspoonful of salt. This would be topped up with water from the big iron kettle boiling continuously over the open fire of the kitchen stove. When the mixture had been stirred into a thick consistency with the handle of a spoon it would then be topped up with milk still warm from the cow. Breakfast was taken quickly, for the horsemen had to be back in the stables for six o'clock, the time they received their orders for the day's work. In the dark mornings in the midst of winter, when it was impossible for the men to go out without lights on the roads of the farmtouns with their horses and carts, they would be given other chores such as threshing corn until the first streaks of dawn arrived.

The day's work got underway as the horses were fully harnessed in their stalls, led out of the stables and yoked to the plough. Much of the ploughing was done in the winter months. But the harsh coldness was refreshing for the ploughman, who soon worked up his own heat from the toil of guiding the horses, keeping the plough properly in the soil and trudging along behind it. It was strenuous work, manipulating the ploughshare through the rich soil with its frosted crust, to form a furrow that was as straight as a ruler's edge. Much of the satisfaction from this toil lay in reviewing the skill with which the furrows were made. A ploughman would take much personal pride in ploughing a field reasonaly quickly, leaving a pattern of furrows which looked as if the design had been set out by an almighty hand.

As the blade of the ploughshare sliced through the soil and laid on its back a ribbon of turf, creating a furrow in which he trod, there was a continuous flow of commands from the horseman to his team. Using monosyllables, he could convey to the horse the orders to start, pull harder, go steady, stop, turn around, restart and the like. When the ploughing was going along in a satisfactory manner there would be

encouraging, though otherwise meaningless, sounds from the ploughman to his pair of horses. Of course the language would become
heated when accidents occurred such as the striking of the plough tip
on a heavy stone or the veering of the plough blade away from the
furrow. At such times the ploughman had to struggle with the plough
to restore it to a fresh line and would hope to cover the site of the
mishap on the next journey over the field. Between the handles and
stilts of the plough the man had to be nimble much of the time. This
was work for men of strength who were also wiry; it was seldom that
one would see an overweight man in this trade.

Ploughing stopped in the morning at eleven o'clock. At this time the
ploughman would unyoke his pair of horses and return with them to
the stable to give them their midday feed. His own simple 'denner' was
usually a more relaxed session at the table then the frantic breakfast
time. After this midday meal the horseman would return to the stable
and join with others for a while seated on the corn kists, the large
wooden chests or bunkers in which the crushed oats for the horses
were stored. With a small group of men assembled and a little time to
spare before starting the work of the afternoon there would be time to
catch up with a few snatches of hearty conversation, some banter,
some coarse exchanges. Generally, the stable was a private club for
ploughmen and normally its social atmosphere was extremely amiable. The ploughmen were ready and free with their help or advice if
someone was in some difficulty with the grieve, with a girl, with his
team, or with some other problem of life.

The work of the afternoon would begin at one o'clock and would
continue without a break until six in the evening or, in the case of the
winter months, until darkness had made it impossible to see the line of
the furrow. Once again the ploughman would unyoke the team from
the plough and lead his horses back to the stable for the night. The
horses would be tied into their stalls, unharnessed, bedded, watered
and fed. Before blowing out the oil light in the stable, the harness
would be set up on the spars on the wall, leaving the great beasts to
rest. For the horses it was the end of the day's work; not so for the
men, for they would usually be expected to put in another hour's
work, perhaps in the barn mill, before facing another day of hard
labour in the field.

In the evenings the bothy men would gather around and indulge
themselves in their life and times, and the people they worked for.
Hundreds of bothy songs were composed by these men; they would

sing them, usually to an appreciative group of other farm servants, in the freedom of evenings. Many of the ballads were about the affairs of work and, of course, all were in the dialect of the district. A few stanzas from one ballad give an indication of the things that meant life to these men while at the same time revealing love and respect for the horses they worked with:

> The frost had been so very hard,
>   The ploo she widna go;
> And sae oor cairtin' days commenced
>   Among the frost and snow.
>
> Oor horses bein' but young and sma',
>   The shafts they didna fill,
> And often needed the saiddler lad*   *whip
>   Tae drive them up the hill.
>
> But we will sing oor horses' praise,
>   Though they be young and sma',
> For they ootshine the neiper* anes   *neater
>   That tip* the road sae braw.   *take
> Sae fare ye weel, Drumdelgie,
>   For I maun gang awa';
> Sae fare ye well, Drumdelgie,
>   Your weety* weather and a'.   *wet

But the evening sessions of ballad singing in the bothy were quite short-lived. The following describes the circumstances of curfew in a typical farmtoun:

> The order was to bed at nine,
>   And never leave the town,
> And for every time we left it
>   We'd be fined half-a-crown.

At that time the average day's pay of a ploughman was half-a-crown. To be fined a day's wages—for work well done—for breaking an arbitrary curfew imposed by a farmer was harsh indeed. At today's prices that daily wage would be the equivalent of £15. This allows us to see that by any standard it was a meagre wage for this mixture of skilled and hard labour.

Although ploughing was hard, it was pleasant and had a great sense of artistry and achievement in it. One major chore for horsemen during the year's work on a large farm was the removal of manure from the farm midden. The work of forking this manure onto carts, leading it out onto fields and spreading it by hand-fork over the acres of ground to be fertilized was physically demanding. Depending on the distance the carts had to go to reach the field where the muck was to be spread, the number of cartloads that could be taken by one horseman each day might vary from ten to twenty-five. It seems that a record of clearing muck by cart was achieved by one Aberdeenshire worker who moved 95 cartloads of muck each day for three days, making a total tonnage of approximately 206 tons—a Herculean performance, both literally and figuratively, one might say. Although it was a stinking job and sore work physically, for those able to do it it represented a great challenge—a major job which had an end to it. As the work progressed the worker could determine the amount of progress he was making with the task before him. Work-games were commonplace with the horsemen, and to some extent they were a means of motivating themselves for chores which were otherwise devoid of attraction.

The hiring of farm servants was done by spoken bargain. It was the usual practice to hire a man at the local fair. The farmer would visit the fair and circulate among the farm workers who were there seeking employment. When he believed he had found a man for a given job he would then bargain with him for the rate of pay which he would accept for a half year at the farm. This would include his board in the form of plain fare at the table. Accommodation would be a bothy which might be a single room with a couple of beds or a larger building such as barracks in which the horsemen's four to six cots were set along each wall.

Inside the bothy there were usually bare stone walls. Bothies were often built over, or at the end of, the stable, or above the cart-shed. Sometimes bothies stood at the edge of the midden for obvious convenience in the total absence of plumbing. Very occasionally, neater, more acceptable, bothies were located above the farmhouse kitchen, having their entrance by a stone stairway from the yard outside. This was home for these horsemen. The horsemen themselves could give little care to these bothies and they were often extremely squalid. It is said that the best bothies were those in the north-east from Perth to Aberdeen. Even there, however, bothies provided very primitive accommodation.

At the end of the era of bothy accommodation one old bothyman

Ploughing traditionally with Clydesdale pairs

described his former style of living to an East Lothian newspaper. Some of his impressions were as follows: 'My first was a hut resembling a pig house, the floor of which was eighteen inches below ground level. In rainy days the water came in at the door and ran out below the wall at the other end. There was no fireplace. I had to walk on planks laid out on the floor to go to and from my bed with dry feet. At this time I was a working boy of eleven years old. My next was a bothy above a stable with horses that had first breathed the air. Rats ran in its thatched roof and scattered dust from the rafters on to the sleeping men below throughout the night'.

One more account of bothy life has been provided by a salesman travelling these areas, taking particular note of the living conditions: 'A bothy was often a low apartment without partitition or ceiling, occupying the space from the gable wall of one building to the gable of another. The overall plan of the bothy, within, was a row of undressed deal-beds along each side. There was a fireplace at each gable end but these fires had no chimneys, only narrow slits in the walls to allow smoke to find an outlet. The roof leaked in dozens of different places and along the ridges of the roof the sky might be seen from one end of the apartment to the other. The men in the bothy learned to tell the time when they awoke during the night by observing the stars which were visible through the openings of the roof. It was, in truth, comfortless habitation for human creatures in a wet and gusty winter's night. The inmates were as rugged as their dwelling place was rude'.

Reports of their conditions did much to ensure the end of bothy-living for these men, but the change was slow. Bothies in Aberdeenshire and the north-east had superior conditions. In some of these, young farm lads were smothered with motherliness, fed like fighting cocks by the farmers' wives. They were given leave to sit at the kitchen fire and here they could air their views and enjoy familiarity with the family. Before going to their cold bothies at night they might be comforted with a large, heated stone wrapped in a blanket or, in later times, an earthenware hot water bottle to warm them in their cold cots at bedtime.

Young men took all this form of life with an air of nonchalance which became their style. When they moved farms they carried their few worldly possessions in their strong wooden chests which they kept at the foot of their bothy beds. These contained their prize possessions such as their horse 'show' harness as well as their own Sunday suits. Many of them moved from one place to the next each half year, almost for the relief which a change provided from the monotony of work. It was only when some country lass got them to the altar that many of them became sufficiently settled to remain permanently in a farm cottage. Even then, the stay might not last much longer than a year— from one Whitsunday to the next year. May 15 (Pentecost) was the traditional Term Day when work contracts ended.

When this form of life in time grew too monotonous and the chances to change farms became few, many of them turned to the recruiting sergeant who seemed to some to be a kind of saviour. The recruitment of men for the regiments of Scotland was a continuing activity, and the recruiting sergeants were almost always present at the hiring fair ready to pay 'the King's Shilling' for any fit young man volunteering for service.

Horsemen tried various pastimes in addition to the invention of ballads. The cart assigned to the horseman was an item which received quite a lot of careful attention. When a cart was in good order and reasonably new it could be gaily decorated for a particular occasion such as a local children's picnic, or a show day, or a day of games at a Highland gathering. On such days farm carts were cleaned, freshly painted and lavishly decorated. The horse drawing this equipage would be groomed to a glossy finish and its mane and tail would be brightly decorated with ribbons and raffia embroidering. Streamers of coloured ribbons would flutter from the high-peaked collar and parts of the harness. The leather of the harness would be polished to a shiny black; iron chains and brass buckles would glisten from vigorous cleaning. Decorative horse brasses hanging from the brow band and the breast strap, or martingale, would receive much polishing so that they sparkled like golden ornaments as the movement of the horses made them swing to and fro. The cart and its occupants would then make way in carnival spirit to the local social event of the year.

Such events would give an opportunity for bachelor horsemen to meet the young women who also had their parts to play in farm life. Horsemen were thought to be particularly competent in winning the favours of these girls. There was a myth that horsemen were possessed of the much-coveted 'horseman's word'. This was believed to be a phrase or two which, when whispered in the ear of a horse, made it into a gentle creature. It was also the belief that this same horseman's word would have a similar effect when the horseman had the opportunity to whisper into the ear of the lady of his choice. Sometimes, apparently, it succeeded. To this day The Horseman's Word is

D

a secret organization of that trade which has never been publicly revealed.

The social exchanges between these folk on festive occasions would be in the form of broad humour. This was only to be expected of people who lived so close to nature. In their society the births of illegitimate children were accepted as a natural part of living.

The farm houses themselves were not places of grim labour and social deprivation. Many visiting tradespeople called in from time to time with their own horses, or traps, or vans. Visitors to the farm would include the smith, carpenter, saddler, shoemaker, tailor and wheelwright as well as general travelling merchants.

Other visitors to the farm included salesmen bringing seed, livestock feed, fencing materials and the like. The occasional visit by the vet or the doctor in his gig also meant drama in the farm. Some of these men would cover fifty miles a day in the course of their work, for which they were not always paid, nor did they always seek payment. On some occasions the doctor attending a needy person in dire illness would render no account. If the vet's intervention was unsuccessful he would do the same. At other times they would be glad to accept payment in kind, such as a box of eggs or a dressed cockerel. These country vets and doctors threaded their districts day and night with their light horses pulling their gigs at the trot. They would attend the animals and the sick equally promptly in the lowliest quarters or the grandest mansion.

Among the most important visitors to the farm was undoubtedly the blacksmith or farrier, for the farm work would grind to a halt if the horses were not properly shod. The work of the smith was not limited to the shoeing of horses; many of the old smiths had a genius for inventing implements of great use in routine farmwork. Smiths would make their own form of plough, their own harrows, their own type of grubber—an implement resembling the plough but having forward directed spikes in place of the plough share. Some of these men advertised themselves as 'blacksmiths and implement makers'. Much of the work of the smith was also connected with the maintenance of carts. The cart wheel needed its iron rims replaced from time to time, and placing a tightly fitting iron ring around the perimeter of the wooden wheel was skilled work.

Often there was a local arrangement for the blacksmith to be

Ploughmen homeward plodding at the tranquil hour

granted a small amount of land to run as a small holding or a croft. He was able to work on this in the free moments between jobs. Some of his jobs were unusual. For example, with the approach of winter all the sheep which had lost teeth were culled from the flocks. These sheep would be butchered and no part of the carcass would be left unused. The head of the sheep was especially sought after for the making of 'sheip's heid broth', and it had to be taken to the blacksmith who would use a hot iron from his forge to singe away all the hair from the skin of the animal's head, which could then be put into the pot with a mixture of vegetables to make a delicious broth.

The routine work of the smith involved repairing damaged ploughs, resharpening the plough share, and mending plough points. He renewed broken blades of binders and damaged spikes on the horsedrawn hayrakes. In the regions of intensive agriculture the smith was so busy that his forge fire was barely allowed to go out from one day to the next. His hammer on the anvil would ring out bell-like peals regularly throughout the working day. It was the style of the black-smith to take two or three hard blows with his hammer on the heated piece of iron on which he was working and, while viewing the worked iron in his long tongs and turning it on the anvil, he would strike his hammer lightly on the anvil two or three times by way of keeping his hammer hand in action during the pause. The tone from striking the red hot iron was dull and soft, while the sound of the hammer head tapping lightly on one end of the anvil was a sharp bell-like peal. The noise from the smithy was music to those who worked and lived within earshot.

Unlike the ploughmen, who were usually short and wiry, black-smiths had to be of bigger physique for the strenuous work of picking up horses' feet, cleaning them, paring them, fitting them with irons and driving home the nails. All this was heavy work to the smith, bent over much of the time at an angle of ninety degrees. Whilst shoeing a horse he would work at full speed, going from the horse to the fire, to the anvil, to the water-barrel, shaping the shoes to the freshly trimmed hooves. A blacksmith would carry out the regular shoeing of about two hundred horses several times each year. The smith was a man of stature in his community in all senses. He provided essential services for ploughmen, and his inventiveness in making special implements and in repairing damaged equipment saved the farm money. The cost of new equipment was high. The way these men took a certain amount of punishment from the horses through an occasional kick also gained them some esteem, for they accepted such accidents as hazards of the trade.

Among horse breeds in general it is doubtful if another compared with the Clydesdale for docility and reliability. A person could work about these animals in great safety. Their feet could be picked up, both fore and hind, to clean and examine them with little prospect of bad-tempered resistance or a viciously directed kick. They were horses, of course, and they were therefore subject to variations in mood, perhaps when they were sore, alarmed or ill.

Rarely did a Clydesdale have a persistently evil disposition. Such a horse would progressively learn various tricks of making life uncomfortable for a horseman such as squeezing him against the partition of a stall, or biting him about the arm and shoulders when his back was turned to the animal. A bad animal was likely to kick out at the horseman when he was busy coupling the long side chains from the collar to the swingle-tree and connecting this to the plough or the harrows. A horse with such vices might be tolerated if it were capable of providing a good day's work once yoked, for the working ability of horses was the source of much of the respect earned from the men who worked them. For a man who neglected or ill-treated his work-horses there was little support among the rest of the crew on a farm. After all, they were the common means of earning a living, meagre as it may seem today.

Some horses had undesirable behavioural characteristics arising from a defective temperament. Occasionally a horse would be a nervous animal and permanently afraid of any sudden changes or any unusual circumstances around it. Such a horse would often balk (i.e. refuse to be driven forwards) when alarmed by some innocuous event in its immediate environment such as a piece of paper blowing in its direction. A horse might be a jibber and go into reverse when alarmed, or attempt to rear up while still in harness. These events, when the animal was yoked within the shafts, or 'trams', of a cart could be fairly disastrous for man, beast and equipment. Occasionally, too, a nervous horse would take the bit in its teeth and run, even though yoked to a heavy cart. Any runaway horse is beyond control and without direction. Runaways spelled disaster and, with the simple bits used on these working animals (ordinarily a bar bit of iron) it was extremely difficult to pull them to a halt when they took off in such a fashion.

Horses were usually broken to 'the chains' or 'the trams' at about the age of three. These represented the two different forms of yoking that the farm horse would encounter in the course of a year's routine farming. Breaking them to the chains simply meant making them accustomed to drawing weight behind them with a chain running on either side, from the hames, on the collar, to a crossbar or swingle-tree behind. The swingle-tree in the course of work would be fixed to the plough, or the grubber, or the harrows. The simplest way to train a horse for this was to yoke him up to a swingle-tree to which a heavy log was tied.

Breaking into the trams meant full harnessing with collar, saddle and breeching. These items of harness would fix the horse to the shafts of the cart. Once broken to the trams, the horse would then be able to accept being yoked to other farm machinery which also had shafts such as hay-rake, hay-bogey, and cart. Of occasional use in breaking would be a sledge with a single cross-bar in front which would be fixed to the harnessing of a horse on either side of it. Working in pairs was another work style to which the young horse had to be broken, since this was a common requirement. It was a sensible way of breaking, to yoke the young horse close to an experienced docile horse harnessed in a cart, then lead the pair through a variety of exercises simulating the conditions of work. Of course, the breaking procedure was sometimes a little more involved than this. The first fixing of harness on the horse could be a hair-raising experience and there was a limit to the extent of simplifying it by allowing the horse to be in the company of another experienced animal in harness.

The irritating experiences of first harnessing were well known to sympathetic horsemen who had the skill to break young animals in. They would take the animal's anxieties into account so as to accomplish the lesson with a minimum of distress. The young horse did not always take readily to an iron bit in its mouth. It was usual, therefore, to accustom the horse to the feel of the leather head collar or halter around its head a time or two before any attempt was made to fit a bridle and bit. Again the bit could be made more acceptable to the horse by smearing it thickly with a tasty substance such as treacle. The tightening of the girth around its chest was perhaps the one feature of this exercise which it disliked most. For this reason some good horse-breakers would firstly set the saddle on the animal's back and lead it two or three times around the yard. The next exercise

Idle moments in horse work (turn of century). Top and bottom—horses and staff on large farmtouns. Middle—visiting the smiddy

would entail the saddle being fixed to the animal with a slack girth. Later the girth would be tightly buckled. It was surprising how these animals caught on to the purpose of these exercises and, given a few days to learn, most young work horses made very good progress with each successive session of breaking.

An important part of breaking a horse was teaching it the vocabulary of horsemen. Once again, the easiest way for a horse to learn this was in the yoked company of another mature and experienced horse. It is said that the average horse is only capable of learning about six words of command, and indeed this may well be generally true. The working horse knew how to respond to specific commands such as 'hup' and 'whoa' for start and stop and it also seemed capable of learning modifications of these commands such as a click of the tongue to encourage the animal to start quickly or move out faster. The horseman could exercise a great deal of control over his animal by using the standard vocabulary of his trade. With the aid of a little reining, the proper vocal commands could make a horse perform manoeuvres around a farm or in the field. Another of the trials facing the young horse on being broken was accepting the collar and shoving into it.

The working collars in Scotland were quite different from horse collars in any other part of the world; they had high and pointed peaks, usually over a foot in height and rising above the level of the head of the horse, so that they could not be opened by unbuckling them at the top in the way other collars are opened for easy fitting. The Scottish collar had to be placed on the horse by passing it up over the face and head and down the neck. Since the shape of this collar was such that its base was the widest part, it was necessary firstly to turn it upside down to push it over the head. The long peak was subsequently turned and pushed upwards so that the collar, partly down its neck, would rotate and slip back to settle on the base of the horse's neck where it rested against the shoulders.

The one advantage of the high peaked collar was that it could carry longer and more elevated hames. The higher hames were not only for decorative purposes, they were also very useful for carrying long reins in a team of horses. This made them particularly useful items of harness for all-round circumstances, for it was sometimes necessary to yoke and rein together several horses to a heavy item of machinery such as the binder. It was not at all uncommon for a team of three to be used to pull a binder since this heavy machinery had to be pulled along on small iron wheels over the soft gound on the cornfield.

Farm horses with very hairy legs and feet were difficult to keep clean and dry in muddy going. The disease of 'greasy heels' was not uncommon in such horses if they were neglected after muddy field work. 'Grease' was a curse for many a farm horse. The problem of greasy heels—a moist eczema on the posterior surface of the pastern—seemed greatest in horses which had leg hair of a bristly type, but the condition was usually the result of a combination of factors. When feet became wet and soiled, foreign matter could become worked into the skin above the heels and below the fetlock by the action of the foot and the friction of the hair. When a horse stood in an unclean stall for long periods, infection invaded the sensitive, damaged skin above the heels and a severe and lasting dermatitis would develop. A long thick sweep of fine silky hair down the back of the fetlock, even as far as the ground, protected and partly waterproofed the flexion surface of the pastern joint and minimized the likelihood of grease. These 'feathered' legs and feet were therefore favoured. In field work white-legged horses were disliked by some ploughmen who could not keep them clean-looking in wet spells. The stained limbs of the horse condemned the horseman as a poor groom in the eyes of a hard boss. Men were quickly judged by the appearance of their horses.

The well-fed appearance of the animals was something over which the horseman himself had relatively little control. The quantity of feed given to the horses depended a good deal on the generosity of the farmer, and some of them were less than generous. In the main, however, it was well understood by farmer and horseman alike that feeding horses properly was in everyone's best interest. After the breakfast feed the horses would be fed twice a day, once at the midday break and once again in the evening. At these times the staple feeds were corn, hay and sometimes sliced turnips. The only time in the year when Clydesdales had a change from the staple diet was when they were put out to grass for a short summer break. In the latter part of May they would be allowed out to grass for a little time each day until they had accustomed themselves to a fresh diet. At this season the hooves had to be well trimmed down and lightweight shoes put on their great feet. The demand on a blacksmith's time at this early summer period was enormous.

The pride in its own Clydesdale, which gave Scotland much of its farm output, was considerable. There were 100,000 Clydesdales around the country—almost all of them in regular work in the

Bonded workers. Horses in pairs were commonly matched

Victorian age. Approximately 140,000 Clydesdale horses were working around Scotland at the start of the twentieth century. The special

100

regard for their native horse was probably one of the few common denominators among Scots who lived in the town or in the country. Perhaps this was the unique feature of the Clydesdale—that he could tread the streets of the towns and the cities as well as he could the fields. While the Victorian streets were in many instances filled with a motley variety of horses pulling vans, gigs, carriages and carts, the real heavy work was pulling coal carts and this was work for a Clydesdale. The municipal work of collecting refuse and chores of urban cartage, were easy for the Clydesdale and the breed was popular with town councils throughout Scotland. Some councils regularly paid top prices for the best available geldings.

The Shire horse in England was something of a first cousin to the Clydesdale and it probably equalled the Clydesdale in brute strength, but those with the experience of working both breeds were usually of the opinion that the Clydesdale was usually a better all-rounder on the farm. It had better legs for farm work and delivered more work for each bag of oats it ate.

Ploughing matches were the highlights of the year for the more highly skilled ploughmen. Few of them would miss the opportunity to enter into the ploughing contest held yearly at the fair closest to them. Many of them travelled far and wide entering major competitions to seek recognition of their skill with the plough. The earlier form of plough used in most of Scotland was the long and heavy implement which had a wooden board to move the turf as it was sliced up and cast it on to its back, leaving a furrow. Other forms of plough came into use later: the Yankee, for example, was one that found some favour in certain parts of Scotland. This was a slightly smaller plough than the traditional one and it was characterised mainly by the high curve of the iron beam which arched upwards, from the point where the two stilts joined together, to the hook which would be connected to the swingle-trees of the ploughing pair of horses.

Another plough soon appeared on the scene. This was the swing plough and it was the one which finally won general approval throughout Scotland by the middle of the nineteenth century. It was a plough which was entirely made of iron and which could be handled fairly easily by one man whereas formerly several men had been required to manipulate the heavy wooden contraptions. The swing plough's popularity was quickly enhanced by the fact that so many of those who won at ploughing contests favoured it. In many cases the handles on the stilts were also made of iron. Many implement makers throughout Scotland were particularly skilled as ploughwrights and a few of them attempted to make improvements on the ploughs of their time. While leaving the basic design fairly standard, they produced modifications to the shape of the mould board (the broad iron scoop which turned the turf over). It was found that the soils of some areas required a different shape of mould board and some localities favoured a plough designed for the soil of that district. Very small and lightweight ploughs, made entirely of iron, were much more popular among smallholders and crofters who had to perform a different type of ploughing. The crofter had to solve problems of tilling over and around stony ground, often with a very shallow top soil and in many cases using only a single horse for power.

Various forms of plough had been developed by the middle of the nineteenth century in addition of the 'swing', and changes also took place in the form of other horse-drawn implements on the farm. As mechanisation increased in the towns, this was reflected in the way farm implements were improved. The reaper was introduced in 1890, and after this the binder was developed. Some farmers thought the binder would be the last word in mechanical ingenuity—it cut the corn and sorted it into sheaves, bound these with wire and discarded them in a swathe behind the machinery as it moved along. In the beginning of binder use, the breadth of cut of the swathes was about five feet; this was later increased to six feet by the 1930s. By this time the binder had been lightened and further developed so that it could be pulled readily by a pair of good horses throughout the whole of a day in the harvest fields. In areas with heavy soil, a third horse had to be fixed in front of the central dragpole. Horse-drawn machinery for harvesting became so efficient that one machine drawn by a pair could cover twenty acres in a day. The age of intensive harvesting had arrived.

7. Clydesdale Business

The Clydesdale's reputation flourished during the nineteenth century at home and on show. The horse drew much admiration from international visitors, and interest in the breed grew throughout the British dominions. In 1840, Canada imported its first Clydesdale stallion, strangely called 'Cumberland'. Three other stallions from Scotland soon followed. Exports of Clydesdales from Scotland progressed from 1850 onwards, at a steady rate, until the Clydesdale Stud Book was published in 1878.

The Stud Book publication stimulated great interest in 'the new breed', particularly overseas. In 1883 a choice shipment of Clydesdales was made to Queensland, Australia. The State of Victoria and the province of Otago, in particular, got many good horses. From 1885 onwards a constant flow of Clydesdales went out to Australia, Canada, New Zealand, the U.S.A., Austria, Russia, Italy, South America, South Africa and other countries. So great was the sea traffic of Clydesdales to Australia that some Scots farmers were engaged to travel with boatloads of horses almost continuously for years. The numbers exported from 1884 to 1929 ran to 19,580 and reached 20,000 when World War II virtually stopped this traffic on the seas.

The great bulk of these profitable exports of Scotland's horses took place before the Great War, with a peak period in the four years from 1908 to 1912, when 5,845 horses in the Clydesdale Stud Book were exported overseas. A few of these fine animals regrettably died at sea on their long voyages, both in sailing ships and steamers, but most arrived in good order. Many went to the far corners of their new-found continents to upgrade local stock.

The Clydesdale was the first of the draught breeds in both Eastern and Western Canada. In Eastern Canada the Clydesdale was eagerly sought for work on hundreds of logging camps. Upgraded horses were produced on a huge scale throughout Canada. The vast territory of Western prairie-land was put to the plough for the first time ever in the 1880s and 1890s by many thousands of immigrants, who needed plough horses. Many horses went into the hands of quite inexperienced

Line-ups of Clydesdale horse about 1912 at the University of Saskatchewan—a Canadian centre of specialization in Clydesdale horses

farmers and it was fortunate that the ideal breed for this predicament had already been imported by far-seeing pioneers.

One imported stallion, 'McQueen', left over a thousand Canadian foals in his new land! To some extent the imported individual Clydes-dales were lost in the crowd of their own upgraded progeny, but the work got done. It was done so well that the ploughed topsoil, hundreds of miles in all directions, kept blowing away in dust storms (seeds and all) for many years. Eventually the dust settled and the horses went back to plough a different pattern. Canadian farmers formed the Clydesdale Horse Association of Canada. They looked favourably and fondly on the 'Clydes' and made efforts to maintain the breed's quality in their own country by selective breeding and frequent replenish-ment.

The importation of pure-bred Clydesdale mares was the obvious way to ensure locally bred stock of pure quality. Some ranches in the West saw the wisdom of this and Dr. McEachran of Waldron Ranch imported Clydesdale mares from Scotland in 1888 to provide the first of their kind in the foothills of the Rockies where they settled well. Other imports then took place into the Calgary area. But it was the province of Ontario, and the township of Markham in particular, which became the centre of Clydesdale affairs, with a veritable

104

community of Clydesdale breeders. As the years passed many others joined the ranks of the importers and breeders of this regal breed in Canada.

In the West, Brandon, in the province of Manitoba, became the horse capital of Canada before Calgary took over. Brandon organised the arrival, sale and distribution of very large numbers of horses, between 1880 and 1915. These horses were mostly Clydesdales, and most went to the Prairies but some went Eastward to Nova Scotia, Prince Edward Island and New Brunswick. Much of this business was organised by a Scottish immigrant, Alex Galbraith, and by Ben Finlayson—an outstanding Canadian horseman. Finlayson did more for the Clydesdale breed in Canada in his day than any other man. He died in 1933 but not before he had imported from Scotland the quality stock available from the leading breeders in Scotland.

Clydesdale breeding farms were duly established in Guelph, Ontario; Calgary, Alberta and Douglas Lake, British Columbia, all of which were—and still remain—outstanding centres of advanced agriculture. The University of Saskatchewan in 1920 was the first academic institution to invest in pedigreed Clydesdale breeding stock. Later, in 1923, the university purchased, among a group of thirteen head of aristocratic stock, a son and some daughters by 'Dunure Footprint'.

In 1878 a fourteen-year-old boy called James Kilpatrick showed a young Clydesdale colt at an agricultural show in the town of Dumfries, where Burns had died eighty-two years before. The colt was nicely named 'Sir Robert the Bruce'; it was one of the equine clan which had become the finest draught horse breed in the history of the world. The boy was to become the foremost personality in developing and promoting the Clydesdale breed and the man who became principal winner of Clydesdale awards for half a century.

The boy's family tree contained Ayrshire farmers including his uncle, after whom he was called. This uncle, on taking over the farm of Craigie Mains near Kilmarnock from the boy's grandfather, founded the Craigie Mains stud in the year 1875. The uncle, who was a bachelor, induced his brother to allow the young James Kilpatrick to move to Craigie Mains and to live, learn and work there. Thus it happened that the sturdy young Jim rode on his uncle's horse into Craigie Mains where he would remain to succeed, in 1895, to the stud of Clydesdales and become the most popular figure in Scottish farming circles for the seventy years following. Perhaps it was significant for subsequent events in the Clydesdale's own history that Jim's family favoured emigration—his father, Allan Kilpatrick, with other members of the family, left for Australia, while his brother went to Canada. For Jim, who had featured as a youth in the show rings, leading various prizewinning Clydesdales on parade for his uncle, it was natural that he should earnestly pursue the business of Clydesdale breeding for the rest of his long life. In his own words he found horse breeding a most fascinating occupation with no finality.

Kilpatrick figured universally in Clydesdale breeding and the promotion of world-class stallions. Many of the progeny of 'Baron's Pride', which he once owned, were exported to Canada and America around the turn of the century and laid much of the foundation of the breed there. The leading award of the Clydesdale world was then the Cawdor Cup, and although 'Baron's Pride' did not win it himself, several of his progeny did so for him. The influence of this horse in breeding was carried down through his son 'The Baron', until the First World War and beyond.

Although 'The Baron' lived only fourteen years, he served many mares and had a chequered career in the law courts. As a young horse, 'Baron of Buchlyvie' was purchased for £750 in 1902 by two Ayrshire farmers, in partnership on the deal. They were the renowned James Kilpatrick of Craigie Mains farms and William Dunlop of Dunure Mains farm. The story of 'The Baron's' subsequent ownership is a legend.

The horse was kept at Craigie Mains for a while before being moved on to Dunure Mains. The stallion's joint ownership continued until he was nine, when a dispute arose. William Dunlop claimed that he had bought James Kilpatrick's interest in the horse on a specified date by payment of £1,000. James maintained that he had set the price at £2,000 and had not agreed to the lower figure. In support of William's claim, a hotel attendant testified that a celebration had taken place at the time of the alleged transfer of ownership and that on the following morning large sums of money were found on the floor, among empty champagne bottles. The first court decision in 1910 was given in favour of James, but a year later this finding was overturned. The case then went to the House of Lords where it was judged that ownership could not be established. It was decreed that the horse should be put up for public auction and the price shared by the two claimants. 'The Baron' was auctioned at Ayr in 1911 before a gathering of 5,000 people in an incredible scene. The bidding opened at £3,000, quickly going to £4,000 with the two original owners apparently bidding against each other. A complete stranger entered the bidding and William Dunlop dropped out. The stranger eventually bought the horse with the final bid of £9,500. Then it was revealed that the stranger was bidding for William Dunlop, who by now had bought the horse three times— according to his calculation. Dunlop used 'The Baron' well, cherishing the horse till tragedy struck. The stallion had his leg broken by a kick from an uncooperative mare and the great horse had to be destroyed. His skeleton has been preserved for posterity in the Glasgow Art Gallery and Museum at Kelvingrove, where it can still be viewed.

A contemporary of 'Baron's Pride' was the stallion 'Hiawatha', born in 1892 and four times winner of the Cawdor Cup. After maturing slowly, as was sometimes the case with Clydesdales with classic form, the horse developed beautiful limbs and great weight of body. It became common for well-bred Clydesdales to be leggy and 'grow up' (in height) before they 'grew down' (with bulk) as their maturity progressed. 'Hiawatha' certainly had this type of development before he became the best show horse in his time. He imparted many of his features and qualities to numerous daughters and proved to be the top 'getter' of good mares such as 'Boquhan Lady Peggie' and 'Lady White'. The latter was owned by Kilpatrick and was one of his champion team of four horses which swept up all the major prizes in the Glasgow Summer Show of 1903. Many 'Hiawatha' stock, in due course, were also shipped abroad. Some good horses were by now being bred in the Commonwealth. The mare 'Donna Roma', one of the descendants of 'Prince of Wales', was sent pregnant out to New Zealand where she gave birth to a colt called 'Baron Bold'. The colt was considered to be the best Clydesdale born in the Southern Hemisphere. Kilpatrick certainly thought so and commissioned the Secretary of the Clydesdale Horse Society in New Zealand to offer his owner—Mr. Patrick—£11,000 for the purchase and shipment of the young horse back to Scotland. Mr. Patrick could not be persuaded to part with the horse, which he kept for breeding on New Zealand mares. Good Clydesdale steeds were now becoming well distributed around the globe and were being shown off with pride in Adelaide, Christchurch, Chicago and Toronto by the beginning of the twentieth century.

In 1905 Western Canada made a bold bid to acquire the best of Clydesdale females. The two-year-old filly 'Rosadora' had just won the overall female championship and also the Cawdor Cup in very strong competition when she was purchased by Mr. W. H. Bryce, visiting

Clydesdales with friends

Scotland from Saskatoon. This was the first Cawdor Cup winner to be exported from Scotland. 'Scotty' Bryce succeeded in acquiring some other good fillies for breeding in Canada with Kilpatrick's prize three-year-old stallion 'Perpetual Motion' by 'Hiawatha'.

Many winning horses—both mares and stallions—represented the

Harviestoun stud successfully between 1908 and 1930. A 1908 winner was 'Nerissa', a mare which was subsequently sold to distant British Columbia, planting the seed of the breed there. Mr.Kerr, of Harviestoun, with a succession of Cawdor Cup-winning mares, took outright possession of the prized Cup in 1913. At one time the largest stud of Clydesdale stallions in Scotland was the Northern Stud at Elgin, owned by Mr. George Ferguson. This stud catered for the needs of horse keepers in the north of Scotland for several years. When the stud was being dispersed in 1922, no fewer than fifty stallions were sold from it. After this dispersal many animals went to Aberdeenshire, which then became the Mecca of all Clydesdale breeders seeking young future champions; and many were found there.

Mr. John McCaig of Challoch, Stranaer was a notable breeder of mares in his day. At one Highland show four of the first prize winners were bred by him. The first female to win the Cawdor Cup was 'Irene', another of McCaig's horses. Yet another winning female from the same stud was 'Snowdrop', a first-prize winner at a Highland Show. For three years 'Snowdrop' had an unbroken run as a show-winner. She had the necessary breeding to do this, for she was considered the best-bred daughter of 'Prince of Wales'. Perhaps the most outstanding assembly of mares was the stud of Mr. S. Mitchell of Boquhan, Kippen. His mares were regular winners, but the most outstanding was 'Boquhan Lady Peggie', already mentioned as the outstanding daughter of 'Hiawatha'. A singularly prepotent mare was 'Townhead Blossom', owned by Thomas Robertson of Annbank. 'Blossom' gave birth to three sons, each of whom won the Cawdor Cup in their time and prime. But the best mare of the 1920s was 'Orange Blossom', from Cambusland. She was first in her class at the Higland Show in four successive years and was an overall champion in 1927 and 1928. She was then exported to Australia and was an outstandingly successful breeder in that part of the Commonwealth, where excellent Clydesdales were doing a great job breaking virgin soil.

Several studs started to have dispersal sales and, although fairly good prices were obtained for a while, these sales announced the impending slump. The Great Depression began to be felt in the heavy horse business of Scottish agriculture. At one dispersal sale twenty-seven good horses were sold for an average price of £54. 'Dunure Regina'—a Cawdor Cup winner—was sold at 62 guineas! It was the beginning of the end of an era. The town of Lanark, however, bravely kept Clydesdale business going briskly for another decade by handling large dispersal sales which put quality Clydesdales into the appreciative hands of poorer farmers for the first time.

When the Depression was beginning to recede, horse orders were again coming into Scotland from Canada and Australia. Kilpatrick responded by making extensive tours of Clydesdale breeding enterprises in both countries. He was regally received everywhere as 'King of the Clydesdales'. He saw and admired many horses all across Canada and around Australia, from Perth to Adelaide and Melbourne. He saw numerous six-horse hitches in Canada, and these imposing horse teams were a novelty to him. He was impressed with the use of Clydesdales in this way to draw large heavy machinery across the extensive prairies at a good working speed. He also took orders for more Clydesdales from several people, acting as the good businessman he was proud to be. *Salaria* sailed from Britain to North America carrying eleven Clydesdales, hand-picked by Kilpatrick. He had selected eight mares and three geldings for Mr. August A. Busch, the leading and most enterprising figure on the American Clydesdale scene, ranching in St. Louis, Missouri. With her equine cargo, the *Salaria* ventured across the hazardous North Atlantic, which was infested with German U-Boats at the time. The *Salaria* was torpedoed and sank; all the Clydesdales on board were drowned. Americans still had not felt the full impact of the Clydesdale horse.

It was strange that so few American horsemen learned the breed's merits. The breed evidently faced some prejudice in the States, for in 1977 one American authority (L. Dale Van Vleck) wrote the following statement which may explain much: 'The fact of the matter is that even though Belgian, Percheron, Shire and Clydesdale breeds were tried on 'native' mares and many fine heavy coach and wagon horses were produced, no American breed of draught horse ever evolved'. This was in spite of a good start when 1,050 stallions and mares were listed in Volume I of the American Clydesdale Stud Book, published in 1882.

In the local delivery of fresh meat and meat products in American cities by the packing houses of the U.S.A., horse teams in hitches of two, four or six were sometimes used depending upon the bulk of the delivery to be made. The six-horse hitch was a favoured unit of transportation. Because of their spectacular appearance, six-horse-hitch teams of Clydesdales served well for advertisement purposes in the meat, beer and grain industries. On the streets and in the show rings there was great commercial competition to maintain the finest

Team work, around 1910, with Clydesdales overseas. Canada (Top L, Middle R, Bottom R). Australia (Top R, Bottom L). Note different formations in top four. Heavy loads of wool and grain (Bottom L and R respectively)

teams. One beer company kept about a hundred perfect Clydesdales at St. Louis, Missouri so as to maintain three matched teams of six-horse hitches involved in their interests around the U.S.A.

The splendour of magnificently trotting Clydesdales in the six-horse hitch, their coats glistening, their manes and tails gaily bedecked with ribbons, was a great spectacle. On the average, the horses in a six-horse hitch weighed over 2,000 lbs. each and drew, at the trot, loads of several tons on two-ton wagons. It was a sight to behold and one to be revived annually in American parades and in even greater eight- and ten-horse hitchings.

The first Clydesdales from Scotland, dispatched by sailing ship to Australia, went out in the middle of the nineteenth century. Australia had no native horses and the Clydesdale was the first draught horse there. It proved invaluable to the needs of Australia at that time. To haul the huge loads of wool clips at shearing time, as many as twenty-six Clydesdales were needed to draw each wagon to port. Another form of heavy wagon was evolved to meet Australian needs of public transport. It was essentially a Stage Wagon and, although it was modelled on the American stage coach, it was much bigger and heavier and could carry up to fourteen passengers. A special type of coach horse was needed and Clydesdales were used in crossing to breed such a coach horse. The Clydesdale played a great and vital role in all aspects of Australian agriculture for the first eighty years of its expansion and development.

Many Clydesdales were exported to Australia, and one attendant travelling with consignments has described how, from 1926 until 1937, he made regular voyages to Australia with about twenty horses in each shipment. So keen were Australian farmers to get Clydesdales that sometimes a boatload would go out to Australia speculatively and be sold at the port of disembarkation without difficulty. Australia bred some of the best Clydesdales in the world. So satisfactory were the Australian Clydesdales that when New Zealand wanted to import good specimens she often did so directly from Australia. Clydesdales were selected, after trying some other breeds, as the best horses for many of New Zealand's agricultural needs. They were found to be particularly suitable both for general farm work and for crossing with smaller horses to produce sturdy little cobs which were dual-purpose since they could be ridden, or driven in any horse vehicle.

Some Clydesdales were sent to Russia in 1886 where they were crossed with native mares of cart-horse type. By 1920 a large number of these cross-bred horses had been obtained and the crosses produced by this breeding programme, which also included some Shire blood, formed the basis of the breed of very heavy draught horse popular in the Soviet Union by World War II. The breed, having evolved in the Vladimir region, was called The Vladimir Heavy Draught Horse. Slightly smaller than the Clydesdale, its appearance was of a thickset variation of it. The Russian horse has many physical and colour similarities to its Scottish antecedents. The Vladimir is an extremely strong and energetic animal with a lively gait and great pulling power, special qualities which it has also inherited from its

Horse-drawn binders at work in grain fields (around turn of century)

Clydesdale foundation.

Meanwhile, Scotland had its own boom in draught horses, generated by the tillage campaign of the First World War. As tractors on the lands were still in their infancy, even in 1918, this created much more horse-breeding business at home in Scotland. The demand for Clydesdales for increased ploughing was matched by the keen demand for Clydesdales for urban haulage work in the growing cities. Around the 1920s the zenith of the work horse's heyday was reached. Prices reflected this—5,000 guineas for 'Bonnie Buchlyvie'; 4,400 guineas for 'Benefactor'; £2,000 for a mare, 'Venda'; £3,000 for 'Rosalin'; 1,550 guineas for 'Lady Alice'; 1,350 guineas for a Boquhan mare. Thirteen stallions, sold at the dispersal of W. Dunlop's stud at Dunure, went for an average of £1,676 each. An offer of £10,000 for 'Litigant' was refused by Kilpatrick. Clydesdales without pedigrees or winners' ribbons were also expensive; they were dearer than the new motor cars which were beginning to take over the roads.

From the 1930s James Kilpatrick really swept up the prizes at horse shows around the country. He won the Cawdor Cup at the Dumfries Highland Show with 'Craigie Beau Ideal', who also won the Meiklem Gold Cup in 1931, the Brydon Shield in 1932 and the overall championship of the Scotstoun Stallion show on four separate occasions. Kilpatrick wrote twenty years later that 'Beau Ideal' proved to be the best breeding stallion he ever had. Three of this horse's sons won the Cawdor Cup. In 1932 Kilpatrick's stud won no fewer than four of the classes at the Scottish Stallion Show, the Meiklem Gold Cup and the Brydon Shield. His horses stood first, second and third in the line-up for the overall championship that year. Some years later his horses won five of the six classes of Glasgow's big annual Scotstoun Stallion Show. He became outright owner of several gold cups through winning them repeatedly in the face of much opposition.

But there were other leading studs in Scotland besides Kilpatrick's. As a successful breeder and exhibitor of Clydesdales Mr. J. Ernest Kerr of Harviestoun, Dollar stood out. Whereas Kilpatrick purchased some of his winning animals when they were young, Kerr bred his own. He bred no fewer than six Cawdor Cup winners and set an unequalled record of success in that championship.

Clydesdale horse sales in the county town of Lanark were among the wonders of the equine business world throughout the first half of this century. They were held seasonally to meet the needs of the work to come, the disposals from work ended, the long-term schemes of

Show hitches with teams of matching Clydesdales: above—six-horse hitch, below—ten-horse hitch (photo courtesy of D. Charles, Saskatoon)

115

breeding, and the offer of fresh youngsters. Lanark served as the supermarket of Clydesdale horse trading. Other towns certainly had their share of this business, such as the adjacent town of Biggar, but by comparison with Lanark, they kept shop on a more modest scale. Some, however, served the breed well as shop windows for this horse without peer. Scotstoun, in Glasgow, carried out that side of the business best. But Lanark was a sight to last a lifetime as a vivid mental picture of horse business on a gigantic scale.

The sale rings went through their business at a furious pace, below tightly packed tiers of farmers who all looked alike. Seldom was anyone seen to bid. The skill of the auctioneers was not so much in their rate of calling the running-up prices but more in their eyesight, or so it seemed. Horses circled the ring a few times, quickly getting their market price, and by the time they were being led out, the next one in was already being circled by those wiry little horsemen. Although dwarfed by their charges, these men were in command of any and every situation in the auction.

The streets of Lanark, especially up the mile of Hyndford Road, were rivers of Clydesdales. Only the River Clyde itself on the low western edge of the town flowed with more vigour. Across the Clyde and up Kirkfield Bank they came in scores, from the west and north of the county of Lanarkshire: their breeding ground—so to speak. On a sale day in Lanark, horses were walked out briskly and led at the trot to show their free style of gait, their soundness and their worth. A Clydesdale at the trot is singularly impressive for he shows he is really going somewhere. Words may not do justice to the heavy Clydesdale's style at the trot, for he shows evident enjoyment in this gait; he shows off then, as part of his buoyant nature. The Clydesdale is shod with the largest horseshoe in the world. Thousands of these, carrying some thousand tons of moving horse flesh on the streets of Lanark, made their own volume of metallic music. The whole carnival of Clydesdale trading has been over for some time now, and although the charming county town now concentrates on sheep and cattle auctions, the older citizens of Lanark remember the dynamic days of Clydesdale business.

8. A Fraternity of Horsemen

Carting was an exacting job of work, not of full trade status, but calling for some keen knowledge of horse, of harness, of loads, of inclined streets and wheeling physics. As a mixture of skill and endurance, its demands on the person were substantial and kept many of its calling in a stunted but wiry physique. Chiefly there was chronic exposure to the elements as they sat on the corner of the cart rumbling along its route. Transporting and delivering the essentials of the new industrial age was the main order of business in the town. They went out each day, coupled to a four-wheeled cart, to carry iron pipes to the men busily building more town. Again they would show an unwatching world the nature of good work. In villages and farms there were milk churns, bags of grain, vegetables and fodder to fetch and cart. This was sober work and at times the horse was the only one in the partnership supplying that.

It was no job for a woman or anyone with sensibilities—walking and working with heavy horses. A careless exposure of a foot to a quarter ton of equine tread was a constant occupational hazard calling for hobnailed boots. Furthermore, horses are inclined to release flatus frequently and in notable volume. The faces of those who sat close behind could receive much of this. Carters were indifferent to such natural innocence. They entertained no notion of social advance. If they had one common trademark it was their slightly outcast station. This was the price to be paid to be close to nature and her affairs. The weatherproofing property of whisky was their trade secret, freely shared, one with another. The comfort of whisky was there too when the horse was lame, sick, recently dead, or a job was lost (which could be often).

But carters were not without some social presence. Their remarks were very direct, between spits. They variously chewed tobacco or smoked a 'thick black' brand of it in their small pipes of white clay. These pipes were particularly short when the stem inevitably became broken. The shortened pipe would have a small clip-in metal cover put on the bowl and it was then smoked upside down, as another trade-mark—aptly called a 'jaw warmer'. The carters wore bright silk necker-

chiefs with the tight knot to one side. They wore broad leather belts—
retrieved from severed harness often—with large brass buckles of
similar origin. The cloth cap was also *de rigueur*, in addition to being
useful to keep horses' excesses, such as sweat, out of their hair. They
did not appear to go bald: these tough little men not given to
unnecessary worry. In due course, they went in and out of the British
army and often as recruits to the Cameronians or grooms to the Scots
Greys—the grey dragoons. They made their presence felt in foreign
campaigns against the French, the Russians and the Indians. In later
life they would have tattooed arms to show and a tale or two to tell on
returning to carting. They would be established carters then, laws to
themselves.

In Glasgow a unique service was created for cart traffic to cross the
Clyde. Horse ferries operated at busy spots downriver from the last
bridge at the Broomielaw. The ferries, which were free, ran throughout the day, back and forth, taking about a dozen horses and carts
each trip. The high-level deck could be raised to street level for ease of
embarking and disembarking. Before the ten-minute crossing, cart
wheels would be chocked to secure the heavy loads for shipyards,
docks and warehouses. The shortcuts these ferries provided saved a
thousand miles of cartage per week and added years of life to many
horses. The ferries at Govan and Finnieston, established before the
Great War, must have carried untold legions of horses. They had
ceased to run by the middle of this century, but not until there was no
further call for them. The city fathers of old Glasgow deserve credit
and acknowledgement for a realistic humane gesture on the grandest
manner. Perhaps they just liked horses and, who knows, maybe
carters too.

At the end of the working day, home in the stable uncoupled,
unharnessed, watered, tied in its stall and bedded, the horse had to
receive its last and principal feed of the day with carefully rationed
quantities of grain and hay. Then, after the harness had been wiped
off, the horse had to be groomed, or at the very least cleaned down.
The old pro would put in an hour of heavy polishing before he (and the
horse) would be satisfied. Well cared-for horses not only looked better
on the street but they seemed to work better too. The horse's hide is
one of its major organs, serving several important physiological
functions. It needs extra attention in a work horse, which is unable to
practise its own grooming activities and is additionally irritated by
dried-on sweat. No other animal can sweat like a working horse; the

man who put it there should take it off—and usually did.

Agricultural carting is a horse of another colour, so to speak. Seldom was a four-wheeler used on a Scottish farm. For one thing the smaller wheels dug into mud and rendered a bogged-down vehicle worse than useless. Big wheels were needed in wet conditions and the high two-wheeled box cart was what carters used around farms. In spite of the seeming simplicity in the design of the typical farm box cart, it was complex enough in its construction. It was carefully engineered to be highly functional in its sundry uses. The tip-up mechanism of the cart was important for clean and quick unloading. Tipping the cart required removal of the linchpin at the front of the box—and close to the rump of the horse. This had to be easy to do for the carter's satisfaction. Again the balance of the box, both for ease of tipping up when laden and for control of pulling down without crashing and crushing, had to be very carefully judged. The cart was good if the linchpin could be removed with one hand, if the laden cart could then be easily tipped with a shoulder under the protruding stump-pieces, if the empty cart stayed tipped till pulled, if the box could be pulled down gently and secured again with the linchpin. Cartwrights had to be a combination of carpenter and engineer to produce a good vehicle, suitable for its job, durable and attractive in style and design. Many cartwrights were in fact joiners who worked hand-in-hand with blacksmiths, for they had an equal share in the production of a cart. The blacksmith passed judgement on dimensions and made all the chains, bolts and iron fittings.

The last operation, but not the least critical one in cart making, was fitting the iron rims on the wheels. For this the handmade rim had to be a little too tight to fit when cold, but, when well heated in the forge, would just slip over the wooden circumference of the wheel. It would shrink on to it securely when cooled again. Each part of a box cart, made in individual sections, had to be soundly constructed and assembled, for these carts had no springs and the roads they travelled on had no smooth surface.

The type of horse most suitable for heavy street work, for example in the dense commercial traffic in the City of Glasgow, was about five to eight years old, fifteen to eighteen and a half cwts.—or 1700 to 2080 pounds—in weight and 17.1 hands high. Such a horse could travel at a good pace with a three-ton load on level streets. In Glasgow, trace horses at the foot of Buchanan Street and West Nile Street were coupled, in tandem hitch, to the shafts of the carts by long traces in

Horsemen proud to pose with their working partners in the carting business on the farm (around 1920)

order to help with the uphill pull of laden vehicles. Clydesdales with relatively short legs and thickly-coupled bodies were best at starting with a heavy load at street intersections, especially those under the control of a policeman on points duty regularly stopping traffic. In crossing Jamaica Bridge in Glasgow city centre, horses had difficulty moving off from a stationary position because of the incline at both approaches to the bridge. Horses working routinely in this kind of work were good for four to six years, but nine years of age usually spelled their retirement as 'aged' animals. The stressed bones and joints gave problems then. Compared with other heavy breeds, including the Shire, the Clydesdales working on streets were remarkably free from side bone and ring bone in their feet, until they were aged from long days of hard work.

When the working span of the day was measured off, horse affairs were usually discussed by horsemen in the luxury of an idle hour or two. General horse lore was kept precise by the honing of comment and counter-comment, statement and story, dispute and declaration. The older horseman was often the quiet one in a typical hearthside discussion as he allowed recounted events to stir his own deep pools of personal history. Some satisfaction was drawn from observing the growing knowledge of the young, which the experience of his own long working life could verify. The rationed comments of the older horseman settled the argument, explained the mystery, and added to understanding. It was fitting that the passing on of hard-won facts and beliefs should be a respected benediction from horsemen who came and went in life, too quickly. It seemed that the horseman passed his peak age as quickly as the young lads became men. The arrival of old age was fast in overworked, thin bodies. The muscles stayed hard but the joints lost their looseness as the harsh wear and incomplete repair of spartan living became manifest in rheumatism and its kindred infirmities. To work like a horse was no mere figure of speech; it was a way of life chosen by some, enforced on others, which left a mixture of pain and satisfaction for the years spent in the company of the big animals.

The horse did not slow up for the older men, moving less nimbly as legs and backs ached with old stresses, strains, kicks and accidents. In all conscience, these big Clydesdale legs were difficult enough to keep up with, when men were young. Boots were hard to lift in the furrows and the relentless steady pace of the horses drained men's limbs of their strength after long November hours behind the plough. A spring day of harrowing over broken ground twisted and turned ankles, stretched and pulled thighs and calf muscles and made the strong legs of fit men tremble with exhaustion at the end of it. But all of this was the price of admission to the fraternity of horsemen. In every horseman's head was an equine encyclopedia with its own bits of mystery. Nowhere was the mystery greater than in veterinary topics and methods.

Although some were superstitious practices, many home cures apparently worked. Turpentine drinks, Stockholm tar pastes, axle grease ointments all had popular use. It was remarkable how most of these remedies only required the use of substances which would commonly be on hand around a stable or farm. But the belief in them was faith itself. No stable was complete without such items, in bottles or tins, on the window ledge accumulating dust. Proprietary medicines were commonplace and many of these had more pharmaceutical merit. Often, in larger stables, they would be found in wooden cabinets or on a shelf high up on the wall, away from swinging harness. A veterinary book would sometimes reside on a high stable shelf for reference in puzzling circumstances. *Mayhew's Illustrated Horse Doctor* was a standard after its publication in London at the close of the nineteenth century. It was so authoritative in style, so packed with wisdom and equine morality that it could not be doubted as veterinary truth. The exaggerated illustrations of horses neatly drawn in over-dramatic poses of despair and distress belonged in horsemen's nightmares. The mystic, superstitious world of horse illness and remedy was well served with such literature. It can still impress and astonish any reader today. Colic was the worst of illnesses, causing the most anguish.

Pain within the abdominal cavity of the horse is its one major foe. The pain of labour in the mare is another matter; here is an animal like none other, which can hide its labour pains from unwelcome watch. Perhaps fortitude, which it seems pregnancy can offer, contributes to this phenomenon in the equine nature. Perhaps the great tubular canal, of the horse's gut, is singularly sensitive to the inflations, twists and blockages which can accidentally disrupt its normal tranquil industry, an industry of converting rough food to fine physique. This abdominal work is maintained with much parting of surplus material to the air and ground. Like much natural abandon it seems often humorous, the way that the bowels of a horse move prodigiously.

Superstition still abounded in the horse lore of nineteenth-century Scotland. The Reverend Walter Gregory of Pitsligo described some of these in the *Transactions of the Banffshire Field Club* in 1890. It seems that mares and foals came in for a great share of this superstition. If possible, mares were not to be allowed to foal in their stables, for any foal born indoors would later be an untrustworthy horse. To counteract the evil effect of being foaled in a stable, however, the foal, when taken out, could be pushed out backwards. Sometimes the stable door would be taken off its hinges and laid flat in the doorway for the newborn foal to be pulled over by the tail.

The first time a mare was taken from the stable after she had a foal it was sometimes felt that her womb needed protection from evil spirits. This could be done by tying to her tail, with red thread, a small cross of wood from a rowan tree. Mares would remain outdoors, thus adorned, for some time. The rowan, of course, was often thought to have mystical protective qualities. Horses kept, out of necessity, in an open enclosure overnight were sometimes given the protection of a rowan twig tied to the tail by a red thread to safeguard them against use by witches. In the freedom of the pasture, horses could run from evil spirits since they had the special power to see them clearly (causing them to 'spook'). There was a belief that witches might use accessible horses in their nightly excursions and expeditions to Spain and mystical Mediterranean lands. Horses were thought to have been so abused if they were ever found in the morning lying sweating in their stalls.

Pieces of rowan tree were sometimes affixed to stable doors or over them as insurance against intrusion by witches. Another tree believed to have spiritual power was the holly. Sometimes horses would have their flanks pricked with a holly branch to give them special protection against all evil spirits. In other instances a branch of a holly tree was fixed upside down on the inside of the stable door. Holly could guard against intrusion by 'the mare' (or nightmare)—a kind of equine goblin which attacked both horse and man in sleep by pressing on the breast to prevent breathing. Twigs of holly were sometimes hung in the sleeping quarters of horsemen to protect the sleepers from 'the mare'.

Horseshoes over doors could also keep away evil spirits and this led to their commonly being nailed up on the doors and propped up on the window sills of stables. In due course this became a practice to ensure general good luck and the horseshoe itself came to have such an association. Later the prevailing belief evolved that the horseshoe should be fixed with the heels up so that the good luck would not run out of it. Unexpectedly finding a horseshoe was thought to be an omen of particular good luck.

When a young horse was to have shoes put on it for the first time it

123

E

was usual to have it done on the farm and to make the occasion a time of some festivity. The blacksmith would measure the young horse for its shoes, make these at his smithy and return with them to the farm. After the horse was shod a feast would follow with the farmer supplying a bottle of whisky to celebrate the event and make it fortunate. Even in later times, the first shoeing of a young horse was often an occasion for several drams among those involved. By this time, however, all superstition and ceremony had gone out of the worthy practice.

Horseshoes featured in rhymes which offered wise pointers:

> John Smith, a fellow fine,
> Can ye shoe a horse o' mine?
> Shoe a horsie, drive a nail,
> Hit a horsie on the tail.
> Put a bittie on the tae
> T' help the horsie climb the brae;
> Put a bittie on the heel,
> T' get the horsie trot weel.

Horseshoes were often fashioned to alleviate a defect or deformity of the foot. They were surprisingly effective.

Many were the universal cures for other defects, but blood letting was the ultimate treatment when all else failed. It called for much sagacity of opinion, some experience, a little courage and the necessary instruments. Each man who practised bleeding owned a fleam—a special multi-bladed pocket knife designed for this operation. How these knives were cherished! They were often of ebony with inlaid ivory or silver. The knife usually had three snap-out blades. Each blade had a short, narrow shaft with a cutting head at the end, like a miniature axe. The shape of the cutting head varied from blade to blade. One head would have a crescent cutting edge, another would have a spade-like shape, another would be pointed, diamond-like. It seemed as though playing cards might have inspired the designers of these blades which were intended to be chosen according to the type of cut to be made through the horse's skin and into the vein. Presumably, the blade with most cutting edge allowed haemorrhage to occur most freely. The one with least effective puncture limited the outlet of blood to a predetermined extent. Depending on the suspected nature of the animal's ailment, and how near apparently to death, a judgement had to be made concerning the amount of blood letting. A half bucket of blood would be an average dose, but a really serious state of affairs demanded that a full bucket be taken. Some horses survived to justify the ritual but most did not. The latter were dismissed later as too far gone for successful therapy. Bleeding was never stated to be a cure for any specific condition, simply the radical treatment for terminal or unresponsive afflictions.

The procedure itself was delicate enough and brief. A noose of light rope, such as a plough rein, was tightened around the base of the neck of the horse which was usually lying ill. This 'choke rope' would cause the jugular veins to stand out on each side of the neck. The blade of the blood-letting knife would be held lightly over the vein. The back of the blade would then be struck sharply with a small wooden baton, or blood stick. Blood flowed from the wound to be collected in a vessel. Soon the choke rope would be released and the flow would diminish to a trickle and stop. The skin wound would only be a centimetre long and it was closed in a quaint and traditional way.

In 1884 Mayhew described the practice in detailed Victorian style in his book *Illustrated Horse Management:*

> Before any attempt is made to bleed the horse, the animal's eyes should be bandaged. Most animals, from natural timidity, shrink, if they can discern when the blow is about to be delivered, and the point of the fleam is thereby frequently displaced.
>
> The sight should be first obscured, then the vessel raised; afterwards, the fleam arranged upon the huge pipe, thus brought into view, when, a sudden blow being dealt with the blood-stick will cause the current to spurt forth.
>
> When the determined quantity has been extracted, remove the pressure below the orifice, and the outward stream will cease; then proceed to pin up. Having rendered the point of a pin somewhat angular, by cutting off the tip, the wire will pierce the integument the more readily. Drive it through each side of the wound, and, being in this situation, twist, after the fashion of a figure of 8, some tow or threads, or a hair pulled from the horse's tail, round its either extremity. Subsequently, remove so much of the pin as may protrude, and the orifice will be closed by what surgeons denominate a twisted suture.

Antisepsis came of age in the treatment of war wounds in millions of casualties in World War I. Surgical procedures were practised more adventurously and more successfully thereafter. The new attitude towards surgery affected the veterinary world. As a result, veterinary expertise developed around the Clydesdale horse after the wartime experiences of 1914 to 1918 had introduced general improvements in the art and science of healing.

The man who set the pace in specialist attention to the veterinary needs of the Clydesdale was Professor Andrew Robb of the Glasgow

Veterinary College. A tall, lean, well-tailored gentleman of aristocratic bearing, his elegant nineteenth-century figure in city stables and the classroom inspired two generations of knowledge-hungry students. He maintained a horse practice of his own in premises on Glasgow's Parliamentary Road, a long, level and broad thoroughfare, well favoured by cross-town, heavy horse traffic. With much imagination, the practice premises incorporated a smithy which produced and fitted the many surgical shoes which Professor Robb invented and designed to relieve the foot problems caused by the incessant hammer of hooves on the hard cobbled streets. His practical experience, sieved through his very keen mind, was conveyed to his students with much conviction. Confident, competent young horse vets emerged and contributed to the Clydesdale world and beyond. Robb impressed farriers, carters, students and colleagues alike. He stimulated his colleagues very successfully, and great Clydesdale vets emerged locally such as Mitchell in the Anderston Cross district, Weir in the Shields Road area, and his own son Harry. The son matched the success of the father for he also became a Professor of Veterinary Medicine and kept the work horse clinic of the practice very active until the horse slaughterers' yard in the east end of the city wiped the streets clean of horses after World War II. In the last year of his long life he inspired the famous television vet—Eddie Straiton—to write a worldwide bestselling book on equine medicine and surgery.

The years between the wars saw the emergence of other veterinary surgeons in Scotland expert in Clydesdale problems, and such names as Gilmour, Andrews, Pottie, Taylor and Thompson still linger in some memories from great contributions to Clydesdale health in that era. The town of Lanark had the services of Peter Wilson as a vet of great renown and remarkable vision during that time. To this day his memory is honoured annually by a special lecture given at the University of Edinburgh in his name. His practice was adopted by Glasgow University as a teaching unit for veterinary students. Since William Dick established a veterinary college in Edinburgh in 1823 the institution popularly called the Dick Vet has been a seat of veterinary learning for the world. Its own Clydesdale specialists in the inter-war, work-horse era included Professor William Mitchell who also studied human surgery and became a qualified medical surgeon so as to learn the techniques and standards of that profession and adapt them to veterinary surgery, the subject which he taught at the Dick.

Professor Mitchell devoted his life to a study of bone diseases,

City carters with their commercial flat-deck carts (World War II)

disorders and damages, particulary in Clydesdales. His was another grand presence, not unlike that of Andrew Robb in Glasgow. Professor Mitchell was many things in his time—a veterinary surgeon, a medical doctor, a cavalry officer, a professor, a Principal of the Dick and the man who saw this college become integrated within the University of Edinburgh. His deputy in the surgery department was

John Burgess. Johnnie became the most skilful Clydesdale surgeon of all time. He developed so many radical operations for the ills of Clydesdale limbs and feet that he had to invent a whole new array of instruments with which to perform them. His style was so workman-like, so bold and so dexterous that his skill remained an object of wonder until it died with him. To a thousand vets who went all over the world from Summerhall Square in Edinburgh, Johnnie was the most beloved and the greatest of horse surgeons. To Johnnie the Clydes-dale horse was the greatest, worthy of a lifetime's dedication.

The provision of veterinary medicine took many forms. Horse pills are 'boluses' and giving a bolus to a Clydesdale—to purge it for example—involved its own little piece of skill. With the shirt sleeve rolled up the right arm as far as possible beyond the elbow, the horse physician held the bolus, usually an aloes-filled gelatin capsule, about the size of a thumb, in the extended fingers of the hand held out in a cone-shaped fashion. The left hand was inserted into the right side of the horse's mouth; the tongue was grasped and pulled well out; it was then half turned so that it became placed between the upper and lower cheek teeth. Facing straight on to the horse, the physic-giver intro-duced the hand holding the bolus well into the horse's mouth. The knuckles were kept against the palate and along the roof of the mouth as the bolus was carried towards the distant throat. Passing between the rows of molars, care had to be taken that no part of the hand strayed on to their grinding surface or against their sharply-jointed edges. With the arm in the mouth to the elbow, the bolus was pushed over the back of the tongue; the arm and hand were withdrawn carefully and the horse was physicked. Remarkably often it was then on the road back to health with busy bowels.

Requiring much more skill and equal delicacy of touch was the job of firing—making scorch marks on the skin with a red-hot iron. The heavy workhorse got many problems about the lower limbs due to tissue damage and strain. Sometimes the bones were stressed at points down the sides of the shin to cause small outcrops of bone to develop on the surface and cause pain and lameness. At other times bony lumps would develop in the vicinity of the pasterns or ankles. Not infrequently the big flat cartilages of the heels would become hard and inflexible as a result of bone tissue growing throughout their sub-stance. These several conditions were called 'splints', 'ring bone' and 'side bone' respectively and they caused chronic lameness. The presence of these small prominences of excess bone caused irritation to the adjacent tendons and ligaments. After the skin had been touched over these spots with a hot iron point or blade, the reaction to the burn could relieve local pain. In this procedure, called firing for obvious reasons, the firing instruments were heated in a small fire, or by a blowtorch, close to the site of the operation. The use of anesthetics allowed the person giving the treatment to apply the hot iron with care and precision. Some operators preferred a firing iron with a pointed tip on one side of the head of the instrument. Others preferred a firing iron with a small axe-like blade. Use of the pointed iron was called pin-firing, and small burned dots could be made over an ankle joint in an effort to penetrate the upper layer of skin immediately over the likeliest 'seat of pain', as the site of the lameness was called. The procedure was remarkably successful though the telltale spots remained over the ankle for life. The blade of a firing iron was used in 'line firing' to produce a feather-like pattern of skin burns over damaged and painful tendons. Some operators took great pride in the designs they fired on to horse limbs, seeing them as something of a permanent trademark. Horses benefited greatly from the long rest from work which followed firing. Perhaps this was the more important part of the treatment and the essence of its fairly frequent success in those days before ethical restraints.

Countless other skills were called for in administering health care to the Clydesdale. Painful joints, in those days before cortisone, were given 'counter-irritant' treatment with 'blisters'. A blister was a chemical substance, often in an ointment, which burned the skin over a broad area sufficiently to cause superficial blistering. The use of blisters called for a judicious approach and skill of application. Working horses had their tails amputated, or 'docked' to a handspan in length. This made harnessing simpler and eliminated dirty tails. Docking a tail as thick as a wrist called for adequate know-how, but vets made light work of it and it ranked with castration as being all in the day's work. It was in the realm of abdominal surgery, however, that the greatest skills lay. Few vets would be willing to incise a Clydesdale's abdomen, to repair hernia or search for a retained testicle, for example. Only a vet's vet would attempt that. When it was necessary, however, it got done, and even if the results varied, the performance was always highly skilled efficiency in itself. No-one was ever left unimpressed who witnessed sterile surgery being performed on a one-ton patient. The organisation of the event called for skilled teamwork of the highest order. The responsibility of the surgeon was infinite, for he was responsible, not only for the life of his patient, but the lives of all those who participated in casting, securing, controlling, anaesthetizing and assisting in the recovery of a potentially explosive, but gentle, giant. Ministering to Clydesdale health was not for the faint of heart. The end had to come to all horses. The following recollection from youth paints a picture of the sad event which could not be avoided.

> The crack of the humane killing pistol told the end of the tragic stable scene to those, in some nearby cottages, by now informed of the situation. All knew the grand gelding—now they knew he was an item of fallen livestock. The mechanics of removing an equine corpse are not simple and burial is a major excavation. In the light of dawn the gelding had been extracted from its stall and his deep grave, in the home meadow, was being completed by a gang of voluntary workers, some from the dairy too. A big bay mare, the other party in 'the pair', had been used to draw slowly, by a swingle tree and a long rope, the finished animal to the edge of the eight-foot-deep hole in the good pasture. Men then worked quickly to sever the rope and remove the mare. As wooden battens and planks were being sought, over in the stack yard, to serve as levers, the ploughman took out his tobacco knife and quickly slashed off some long strands of hair from the gelding's forelock and surreptitiously tucked them into his waistcoat pocket. Later it would become a tightly plaited little momento. The burial thud touched each stomach but all those there in the brightening light of the day hurried to fill the soil in and over. The chores of farming could not wait for a dead horse. The ploughman, broken that little bit more by the natural harshness of life, went back more stooped, to his cottage. His wife waited to take off his boots, put his cold feet in a tub of hot water and wonder when the lease of her home, the tied cottage, would now end. Her widowhood from the earth and its worker might start soon.

Reputations for horsemen's skills were hard to gain. Much information in their trade would be their secret. Horses were bread and butter to the whole fellowship of horsemen who shared all the same trials of work. Such trials could make men. Robert Burns, the Mossgiel horseman, found inspiration as he trod the furrows behind Scottish horses. In the auld farmer's salutation Burns writes of the horse as follows:

> When though an' I were young an' skiegh (skittish)
> An' stable-meals at Fairs were dreigh, (dreary)
> How though wad prance an' snore an' skreigh,
> A' take the road!
> Town's-bodies ran, an' stood abeigh, (aside)
> An' called thee mad . . . .
>
> In cart or car thou never reestit; (rested)
> The steyest brae thou wad hae fac't it;
>   (steepest hill)   (have faced)

The tranquil industry of harvesting on Scottish farms (pre-World War II). Mid-right and bottom right—stacking corn; others—carting hay

> Thou never lap, an' sten't an' breastit,
>   (leaped) (reared) (sprang forward)
> Thou snoor't awa . . . .
>   (jogged along)

Carting on the farm using the traditional box cart (pre-World War II)

We've worn to crazy years thegither;
We'll toyte about wi' ane anither;
 (totter)
Wi tentie care I'll flit thy tether,
 (attentive)
To some hain'd rig, (reserved field)
Where ye may nobly rax your leather,
    (stretch) (hide)
Wi' sma' fatigue.

These lines show us the extent to which the Ayrshire man appreciated the ways and the world of the horse. They show clearly how Burns loved horses truly and respected their 'pith and power'. The working horse brought home to the poet some of the fundamental features of the reality of life, its harshness and satisfaction; that life presented both impediments and peace. The whole notion of generous thought for the animal was Burns himself. The real Burns of harsh, even coarse, commentary and sensitive, even sentimental mood shows clearly. His own special, poetic vein was influenced in no small measure by the dumb creatures for whom he had such understanding and fond regard.

9. The Canadian Cousins

While Scotland seemed like the edge of the Old World, it was also a stepping stone to the new world of North America. It was no more than fate, perhaps, which determined that many of Scotland's people would be used to bridge the North Atlantic water as folk-stock suited to the challenging conditions of the gigantic new land. Enforced and encouraged expatriation spurred them on their way to Canada. Any new country is required to go through an initial phase of basic lifestyle before a complex society can be structured. The expatriated Scots were needed by young Canada as much as any Victorian maiden needed a good husband. No part of Canada failed to receive Scottish attention of the kind that made farms out of virgin wilderness. Scottish labour went into Canadian acres, whether fertile or infertile, with much sweat and commitment to the broad continent as Scots set the pace for other nationalities emigrating to British North America from the crowded lands of Europe where farm land was unobtainable.

No one can live the basic type of life without the use of animals. The proper use of animals requires much knowledge of them and association with them. An apprenticeship with elders who possessed a lifetime of experience in all the ways to use their livestock was the good fortune of every interested young person in a rural Scottish community. With such a completed apprenticeship such a person was a natural pioneer.

No opportunity for rural self-achievement through effort was possible, or is possible, wherever land ownership was or is not based on a manifestly equitable system. Land ownership in the Scottish glens was feudal under the clan system, but at least that was a system. When the clan system was destroyed after the middle of the eighteenth century no land in the Highlands was owned by the people who inhabited it, worked it and maintained it. Not exactly an equitable system! It is much better today, but in the meantime—for two centuries—the best of people too often walked out of their homeland hating such unfairness with a passion. Still they loved their old country—its air, at least, had been theirs to breathe fully; its history had been theirs to inherit; its totality was there to see and feel. Without owning one handful of soil there was much to possess and as much to leave when their ships sailed and their roots were severed.

In Ontario, the earliest large-scale Scottish settlement occurred in the Guelph township of Wellington County, in 1827, with the arrival of a mixed group of tradesmen, retired soldiers and labourers from the county of Aberdeen, and the Highland counties of Ross and Inverness. Although they arrived in Guelph in debt, they were not paupers. By the early 1830s, many of the original group of settlers had resettled in the neighbouring townships, having finally liquidated all debts. The second of the large-scale Scottish settlements in Wellington County occurred in 1828. Although christened 'Paisley block' by Dr. Dunlop of the Canada Company, whose lands near Fergus the settlers purchased, the bulk of immigrants were from rural Ayrshire, giving an essentially Lowland presence in the County.

In time the movement to this locality attracted leading business and professional men from Scotland, such as Alexander D. Fordyce Sr., who was the first Warden of Wellington County. Another of that vintage was the Rev. Patrick Bell who became the inventor of the reaping machine. Men of this calibre provided the basis for a permanent settlement of lasting importance to Ontario. Interest in Canada grew in Aberdeen and, on behalf of interested parties there, Mr. George Elmslie was appointed to search out a suitable location for settlement. In 1834, he departed for Upper Canada, with letters of introduction to the Lieutenant-Governor. He met Mr. Alexander Watt, a neighbour from home, and his party in Quebec; together they investigated and purchased land immediately following this.

A number of small Gaelic-speaking settlements were established in Ontario in 1840 by emigrants from Kintyre, Argyllshire, Perthshire, Inverness-shire and the Isle of Arran. They were joined in 1848 by a group from South Uist, evicted forcibly when the island was sold to a Captain Gordon. Among the first priorities for their settlements, apart from the immediate need for temporary accommodation, were establishment of churches, schools, libraries, temperance societies and choirs setting decidedly cosmopolitan and ambitious tones for settlement life. Such settlements soon needed horse power and they sent to Scotland for this.

As the vast lands of Canada fostered Scottish immigration, the Clydesdale horse too was absorbed by the Dominion. Although many horses sailed from the Clyde to the ports of Halifax and Montreal, the destination for most of them was 'Upper Canada', as Ontario was fondly called for a time. Some nineteenth-century shipments of Clydesdales were selected and arranged by William Dick, the founder of the Royal Dick Veterinary College in Edinburgh. Dick was the son of a master farrier at White Horse Close in the Canongate of Edinburgh which was the post for the London stage coach. Dick was a man of vision and knew horse flesh well.

By the twentieth century some notable Canadian dealers arranged their own shipments. Mark Duff brought many Clydesdales into Ontario from Scotland at the end of World War I. Nelson Wagg of Toronto was another leading importer of Clydesdales during the 1920s. Many of these horses were collected in the town of Fergus which was a common starting point for them on the long rail journey to the West. Carloads of Clydesdales rolled westwards from 1905 for thirty years from Fergus.

When the first Stud Book of the Clydesdale Horse Association of Canada was published in 1886 it contained no fewer than 563 pure-bred animals; by this time 243 were mares. By the middle of the next century the number of Clydesdales which had been registered in Canada had risen to 90,947, with a fair proportion of these imported. In one single year, 786 new registrations were entered, with Ontario and Saskatchewan leading all other provinces, with 256 and 207 respectively.

Strangely enough, American breeders had beaten the Canadians in the formation of a Breed Society, for the American Clydesdale Association was formed in 1879. But the truth of the matter was that many of their registered horses were, in fact, Canadian. Many more Scottish Clydesdale stallions went to Canada than to the U.S.A. where the early seeds of the breed apparently fell on some stony American ground. Some good Canadian Clydesdales did go to the U.S.A. occasionally to collect trophies at major exhibitions and international fairs there. One very fine Canadian filly found its way back to Scotland via the Chicago International Fair where it was grand champion. At the World's Columbian Exposition at Chicago in 1893 no fewer than twenty Clydesdale breeders from Canada had entries. During the ten years, 1920-1929 inclusive, Canadian-owned horses won the American Clydesdale championship.

In 1911, the Clydesdale Horse Association of Canada published Volumes 1 to 18 of its stallions. It covered 10,374 registrations of stallions in the country up to that time. The columns of highly-bred Clydesdale studs looked like a mirror image of the Scottish scene in

Large-scale grain harvesting with horses on Western Canadian wheat fields (around 1910)

horse breeding. All the good lines were represented. Most noticeable were the numerous sons of the prepotent 'Baron's Pride' which shaped the Clydesdale in its refined form. Notably, the foundation sire 'Glancer' had three Canadian sons in the first volume of the new stud book.

Canadian-bred stallions carried such names as 'Ottawa's Prince', 'Ontario Chief', 'Ontario Type', 'Pride of Ontario'; there were three 'Maple Leafs' and no fewer than eleven named 'Pride of the West'. Two were named simply Saskatchewan. In Alberta several stallions had regal names such as 'Alberta Chief', 'Alberta Prince' and 'Alberta King'. The 'Boys' were popular across the country with 'Columbia Boy', 'Alberta Boy', 'Western Boy', 'Ontario Boy' and 'Gay Boy'. In fact there were forty-one 'Gay' Clydesdale stallions listed innocently. Canadian breeders gave their stallions the name 'Lord Roberts' more than any other single name and there were 200 'Sirs' of varying appellation in these far-off imperial times. Others favoured more apt and humorous names such as 'Romeo' and 'Robbie Burns'. Scotland's native poet hero could, of course, have given any 'Romeo' in the world a run for his money, it was believed.

William Taylor Sr. of 'Clydelea' farm, Ontario started in the Clydesdale business early in the century with a filly called 'Rose' which produced sixteen filly foals in a row and never missed a year until she died aged eighteen. William Taylor Sr. won numerous national trophies from 1914 onwards. He also shipped Clydesdales westwards and sent about thirty horses (mostly stallions) per trainload to the west from 1923 throughout the remaining boom years of the horse in western development. His son 'Bill' followed in his footsteps to become the leading Clydesdale figure in Central Canada by the middle of the century. His grandson became the first man to demonstrate the operation of a six-horse hitch at the Royal Highland Show in Scotland.

The six-horse hitch was a Canadian invention produced in 1928 by Cecil Leslie of Saskatchewan. He demonstrated this hitch of Clydesdales at the Royal Winter Fair Exhibition at Toronto. To the amazement of all the spectators at the event he could control the team of six and bring them around in any direction simply by whistling. Of course Western farmers had been working with big teams of horses in various hitched-up arrangements from the early days of prairie ploughing. This was what their working lives were concerned with—the tillage of endless acres of virgin land.

When the Canadian West became developed as a great farming

area of the world, the need for heavy horses there became great. In a short period of time at the close of the nineteenth century the provinces of Manitoba and Saskatchewan, in particular, became a stronghold for the heavy horse, and by 1906 these provinces had a total of 176,000 working horses on 23,000 farms. The Canadian West had been developed by this time into the most fertile expanse of cultivated farmland in all of the world. Here the Clydesdale was far and away the most popular breed of horse in those days. The uniformity of the breed allowed many people, with only a limited prior knowledge of heavy horse management, to take appropriate care of these animals.

Western farmers were much preoccupied with their horses since they required continuous care throughout the seven-day week. Each day there were the morning duties of watering, grooming, harnessing and feeding these animals, and the stable had to be cleaned each day. This made early morning work for these horsemen-farmers, for these chores had to be completed before the day's work on the field could begin. The horsemen were required to feed the animals supplementary rations to compensate for the long hours of work in the fields. They followed an old rule for this feeding; one pound of grain per day for every hundred pounds of body weight. The average Clydesdale got seventeen pounds of grain daily; a quarter of this would be given in the morning, half in the middle of the day and the remaining quarter at night when its day's work was finished.

Great care had to be taken of these animals at work in the heat of scorching prairie summers. The vigilant farmer would regularly check underneath the collar to determine that no pressure sore was developing. At the same time excess sweat could be wiped away from the area where the neck blended into the shoulder. Any harnessing sore developing had to be given instant attention, for any horse with a collar sore could not be harnessed for work for some time and would be a real hindrance to cultivation or harvesting. If a horseman found a small area beneath the collar where there was skin abrasion he would quickly apply a sweat-pad between the collar and the horse, and often this was all that was necessary to prevent development of a harness sore lasting throughout the work of the season.

With the great increase in horse population on the prairies it followed that much horse-trading was done. For the first decades of the century almost every freight train westbound from Ontario carried with it numbers of working horses, and sometimes imported stallions, destined for the provinces of Manitoba and Saskatchewan. In Manitoba, Brandon was the focal point for heavy horse traffic, while in Saskatchewan both Regina and Saskatoon were centres where heavy working horses were bought and sold by farmers and dealers. It was the elite of horse traders who were found specializing in imported pedigreed Clydesdale stallions. These animals represented the most expensive of their tribe and the scarcest commodity. Prices up to $10,000 were paid for such stallions. The marketing of purebred Clydesdale mares followed soon after the market had been opened up by imported stallions. Horse dealers tended to operate close to these main centres of pedigree horse-trading. At Brandon, for example, there were twenty-three livery stables and as many horse dealers in the year 1886. One company of dealers paid out a total of three million dollars for horses around the year 1883.

The Province of Saskatchewan, with one million horses, was then realising its potential for extensive cultivation, for it contained half of all the arable land in the Dominion of Canada. Top-quality draught horses had become the principal need of grain-growing, pioneering settlers. Since a number of these were Scotsmen, with fond memories of the work horse of their native land, the Clydesdale became supreme on the agricultural scene there.

In most of these transactions involving the export of Clydesdales, a prominent part was played by Mr. Kilpatrick. He received visitors from overseas at his home, took them to see Clydesdales on show and introduced them to Clydesdale breeders from all parts of Scotland. Kilpatrick exported some of his own better horses. In 1912 he travelled to Canada himself and tried to purchase a farm adjacent to the Guelph Agricultural College in Southern Ontario. Guelph has Canada's premier Agricultural and Veterinary Colleges, and it was shrewd of Kilpatrick to try to get a foothold there. The purchase of the farm did not occur but much goodwill for Scottish Clydesdales was established. Mr. Kilpatrick went out west and bought farmland in Saskatchewan. Again he promoted the breed there, where a Mr. John King farmed and became a major importer of Clydesdales. In 1913 Kilpatrick participated in the export of good fillies to the U.S.A., including a Royal Show winner named 'Craigie Sylvia'.

The working horse helped to establish an agricultural empire in Western Canada. But the Clydesdale did not have it all its own way. Although it had a massive following of supporters among the Scots farmers of the region, other farmers not formerly acquainted with the breed perhaps did not have the same love for it and showed some preference for Percherons and Belgians. These became increasingly popular as time went by.

The Shire from England quickly fell from favour, and by the year 1900 there were very few indeed in Western Canada. Clydesdales were the most popular for much of this same time and the popularity of the breed was evident when horses were being shown at agricultural fairs. In the year 1900 at the Toronto Exhibition there were 875 horses entered and the Clydesdales overwhelmingly dominated in the draught section at this show. Without a doubt the farmland of the Early West was won over by the Clydesdale.

In due course rural communities found themselves divided on the issue of which was the preferable breed. It seemed for a time that no one was neutral on this issue. One side favoured the hairy-legged Clyde with its superb action while the other preferred the heavy muscling of the 'European' breeds, which also had a slightly more phlegmatic temperament than the Clydesdale. It seemed that the difference of opinion would never be resolved, and Scottish settlers remained committed to their horse.

In some communities of the West the feelings among farmers were so strong that friends of the Clydesdale horse occupied one side of the judging ring while those who favoured Percherons and Belgians assembled on the other. When graded, or half-breed, Clydesdales were being brought into the ring there would be cheering from the appropriate group followed by counter-cheering when the opposing group observed a horse of their chosen type coming into the ring for the judges' attention. The keenest rivalry centred on draught mares and geldings, shown either in the halter or in harness. On these occasions the Clydesdale with its stylish gait and its gaily splashed white markings and bold demeanour tended to win most of the attention and most of the prizes.

In some cases teams of horses were shown, as many as six horses comprising a team. Among these team events the Clydesdale had an almost unbroken record of winning in agricultural shows throughout Western Canada for many a decade. As the years went by, however, the number of Percherons and the number of Clydesdales gradually evened out so that by the time steam-driven tractors started to compete with the draught horse for supremacy on the plains these two breeds were equally favoured in Prairie agriculture.

With the appearance on the scene of tractor power, there was an obvious threat to the continuation of the heavy horse as the mark of power on the Prairies. As time went by new models of tractors were appearing on the Canadian scene to facilitate the agricultural work and at the same time to perplex the horseman. Those concerned about the horse industry and the horse's role in Canadian farming were anxious to establish fresh interest in horses and their merits. They sought to provide something dramatic and instituted horse-pulling contests around the smaller agricultural fairs.

By 1921, horse-pulling contests were becoming fairly commonplace events, attracting enthusiastic observers at agricultural shows. It was for a while difficult to ensure that there was uniformity in judging the power of the pull of any given team of horses. A device called a dynamometer was created to register the power of pull. It was an American invention but was quickly adopted throughout Canada to judge more precisely the pulling power of any team in a contest. Soon there were uniform rules in these contests making use of this machine, and Western Canadian horses started to make world records in pulling power. The first world record documented for a pull by a team was notched by a Clydesdale pair in Calgary in 1924. This team pulled a total of 2,615 pounds a required distance of 27½ feet. Later this record was broken by a team of Percherons, and thereafter the world record in horse-pulling was broken quite regularly at agricultural shows throughout the Prairie provinces and Western U.S.A.

All of this helped to draw attention to the value of teams of horses rather than the merits of individual breeds. There was no denying the important economic benefits which would come when farmers could use larger teams of horses requiring fewer men to drive a given number of animals. With proper hitching, one man could readily handle twelve horses. Even huge teams of sixteen and twenty could work together under the control of one man.

A twelve-horse team pulling three seed drills could plant approximately eighty acres a day. Such a team, depending on the nature of the soil, could draw a three-furrow plough, to turn eight acres a day. These large teams of horses could be assembled either in breadth across the front of the machinery or they could be extended forward from it in pairs. Some farmers favoured twelve horses strung out in six pairs behind one another, while others preferred two rows of six horses side by side in front of the vehicle. One point in favour of horses working pairs behind one another was that they were easier to control than when they were spread out side by side. Adjustment of the horses to each other, and to the equipment, was most important in these large

Clydesdale crosses at work in the Canadian winter. Left—Eastern Canada; right—
Western Canada

teams. With correct hitching it was possible for the horseman to drive
the lead team and allow the rest of the horses to pull behind them as
followers under self-control. Twelve-horse teams became widely
favoured. One farmer observed that it was as easy to drive twelve
horses properly hitched as it was to drive a single pair. This attempt to
improve the working efficiency of agricultural horses by using them as
large teams persisted for a time. The revolution of mechanisation on
the farm was still to come.

In the 1930s in Western Canada a combination of drought and
economic depression cast a spell of despair over the Prairies. Even
tractor sales fell away abruptly, almost to nil, as the Depression went
further and further downhill. Prices of agricultural produce and
animals became so low that it was difficult in many cases for farming to
continue at all. In particular, food prices plunged to such low levels
that it spelled the ruin of many farms. Prairie dust storms became

commonplace and did nothing to disperse the gloom which had settled over the whole region as a result of the economic disaster in the rest of the world, of which Canadian farmers had very little understanding. They readily understood the reality of poverty on the farm, however.

Fortunately the pioneering spirit of these people was still very much alive and their resourcefulness in dealing with the problems of financial ruin, farming poverty and the like was a testament to their determination. Fuel for tractors could not be afforded so that the age of horses returned. It was hard on these horses which were brought back from semi-retirement to active field work, for many of them had grown soft from lack of work. Although the numbers of horses in the community had diminished in the face of competition from the tractors, there were sufficient of them in early retirement throughout the area to be brought back into the work force and to perform most of the essential operations in the wheat-growing lands.

Imports of tractors to Western Canada fell from 21,000 in 1929 to as low as 2,000 in 1933; horses were the only hope for agricultural survival for most people. Farmers were glad, indeed, to have the horses once more to see them through the Depression. Many of them said that never again would the mistake be made of ignoring the horse's vital role in farming. The farm horse had returned by the mid-30s from an unimportant position in farming to the mainstay of all agricultural operations, serving in many cases in the same way as in the pioneering years. This horse era lasted as long as the Depression. For example, Saskatchewan, which had a million horses in 1929, still had 800,000 in 1940—although many were old and perhaps not capable of a full day's work in the fields.

Scotland's great horse, once an essential worker on Canadian fields for over a century, was part of the history of this worthy, striving land.

In recalling, in a letter, the last days of great working horses on the Prairies, a famous veterinarian—a farmer's son of Scots decent— provided the following personal reminiscences: 'When I was young, before and during World War II, all our farm implements were pulled by horses, but of the eight horses Dad owned, only two were purebred Clydesdales; the rest had some Standardbred mixed in them. I suspect that if the gasoline tractor hadn't been invented that a breed would have developed out of that mix. Most of the farmers in the area used that or a similar cross (Clyde X Standardbred), although there were a few purebred advocates. The Clydesdale was not always the most popular in Western Canada; there were also the Percheron and

Steam power taking over on the Canadian prairies (around 1920)

the Belgian. Some people thought these were easier to feed and to handle than the 'Clyde''.

'The spring I was six years old I stayed home from school a lot to drive four horses pulling a 'packer' to smooth the field following its seeding by Dad who had another four horses on the drill. I can't recall driving more than two horses for a couple of years after that; then when I was about 12 I drove four on a binder for a few days, and at about the same age I drove six on a cultivator for some weeks. We got our first 'field tracks' the year I was ten but it only gradually replaced the horses. We continued to power the threshing machine with steam until help became so scarce in W.W. II (I think it was 1941), we went to combining the crop. That was a dramatic change. In 1940 the threshing was done with 11 or 12 or 13 people; in 1943 there were only three of us on this work.

'I think that only when I drove the six-horse team did I have a pure bred Clyde except for a few times that one was in one of the two-horse teams I used. This pair was a quiet slow old mare and her gelded Clyde-bred offspring who was the fastest horse on any team. He had a wall-eye and stringhalt and a mildly crazy disposition, but was the 'workingest' horse I ever saw.'

As World War II came to a close, horse slaughter plants were established in various places and this marked the demise of the working horse on prairielands; by this time the development of tractor technology was such that no horse team could stand the competition. Tractors up to 70 horse power were being marketed widely. These new mechanical giants had a wider range of capabilities in the field. It was their new versatility as much as their new-found power which made the contest between tractor and horse an unequal one for the four-legged workmate of the Canadian farmer.

As often happens, one man's loss became another's gain. Not all of the unwanted Clydesdales on the Prairies went for slaughter or discard, some found new working lives back to the eastern side of the country, and in Newfoundland, for example, where extensive virgin timber was available to the pulp paper industry. Trees required to be hauled out from places inaccessible to tractors. In the 1940s the pulp production in the Island of Newfoundland, Britain's oldest colony, was in top gear. Clydesdales arrived from the North American mainland and from the Canadian West in particular. A big timber operation could use a hundred Clydesdales among its numerous crews of loggers. They were suitable horses for the job although they were not handpicked and a few were 'hard cases' which had survived the Depression years. The men who worked these animals mostly had their prior horse experience with the Newfoundland pony and they marvelled at the style and performance of these huge workers. The

Clydesdale had once again won the respect of men of iron. Better than horse fanciers, they could appreciate this horse's qualities of heart and sinew.

While Scotland was adding an average of 2,000 new entries per year into her Clydesdale Stud Book in the early part of this century, an average of 800 additions per year were being listed in the records of the Clydesdale Horse Association of Canada. The Canadian association, which was formed in 1886, had registered a grand total of 50,000 pedigreed Clydesdales before World War II. From then onwards, the Clydesdale Horse Association of Canada was blessed with a long-serving secretary, Doug Charles, who, for a lifetime, kept the statistics of the Association in meticulous order on behalf of its hundreds of members.

10. The Shetland and Others in Service

One of the chief wonders of the equine world is the Shetland Pony. The insular and northern families of pony, particularly on the smaller islands of Shetland, are constantly subjected to strong onshore winds. At the same time they are deprived of shelter in their treeless terrain. The pony's thermo-regulatory adaptation to this is a reduction in physical size, including limb length. This is a most proficient means of body-heat conservation. This, briefly, has long been the conventional explanation of the Shetland Pony's form. While adaptation has undoubtedly occurred progressively, the key to this pony's physique lies in a mutation. A mutation is a major and sudden genetic change, and many forms of mutation are recognised in biology. The type which evidently occurred in the creation of the Shetland pony is induced mutation. It probably took place in one family of animals, and these individuals were induced to flourish in their natural niche, to the ultimate exclusion of any others around less physically suited to the local circumstances. This mutation may have occurred on Shetland or it might have taken place in some Scandinavian spot. Small horses would surely have been an attractive proposition for Norsemen to take in boats on voyages.

The pony's true origin is unknown, but it is probably of Norse origin. (It is certainly free of any trace of warm-blood ancestry.) Records of its existence in the Shetlands date back many centuries to times when these islands were under Viking settlement. The Shetland Islands were a natural nursery for the close breeding (and inbreeding) of insular stock which could be transported by small boats. That its diminutive size is no longer due to the severe climate of this region is obvious from the fact that many generations of specimens bred in more benign locations, such as Southern U.S.A. and elsewhere, have not increased in size. In the islands the pony certainly has much to endure, especially at the end of a severe winter and before the spring when grass is slow to grow. It often has to rely on seaweed for its food when it fends for itself in the wild state.

Shetland ponies were used in various ways by the people of the islands. They were particularly suitable for carrying peat from the bogs to the homes. For this work they were saddled up with a pair of wicker panniers which would be filled with the peats, when cut and dried. Strings of laden ponies would be driven by several islanders, each person being responsible for a number of animals. The group would make its way homeward as one unit. This was a common sight up until the start of World War I. The small Shetland ponies were also used in carting peat and seaweed, and in connection with fishing. They carried basketfuls of fish from the boats to the fish sheds and houses. Although not used in ploughing, harrowing-in seed in the spring was one field job carried out by these ponies, even the very small ones. Two sizes of Shetland pony were commonly recognised. In time the very small ones became the most valuable, and at one time young foals of the small variety were valued at £100 each. Many ponies went to the mines throughout Britain, others became pets and found their way, as such, to all parts of the world. They became very popular in the U.S.A. as riding horses for children, and the American Shetland Pony Club was organized in 1888 to cater for the wide American interest in the breed.

Small breeding studs thrived in the Shetlands, the numbers of these varying with market values. The Shetland Pony Stud Book Society organised its stud book which in due course became the responsibility of their dedicated registrar, Mr. Paterson of Arbroath. Registered breeding and the records of pedigrees ensured the continuity of the breed in pure form, although 'half-breed' ponies were in common use in the Shetlands where they were more useful for heavier work. Lord Londonderry established a stud in 1870 in the islands of Bressay and Noss; his stallion 'Jack' was a foundation sire with a profound influence on the breed as it is today. Other notable breeders such as Andrew Manson in the Shetlands and J. Kerr of Dollar kept refinement in the breed. For the larger variety the height was slightly over ten hands (102 cms). The smaller variety even went below 8.5 hands (82 cms). An ordinary size, about two centuries ago was apparently nine hands (or one yard) and, even at that time, some were less than 30 inches or 7.5 hands high. Clearly, the very small Shetland pony is by no means a modern product.

In 1845 their circumstances were described by the Professor of Agriculture at Edinburgh University as follows:

> These little horses in their native islands are left almost in the state of nature until they are caught for use. They have no shelter from the continued storms of tempestuous seas, beyond what the crags, ravines and sides of hills, afford; and

they scarcely ever receive any food but what they can collect on the sedgy bogs, the heathy hills, and barren shores of the country. They are thickly covered with a coat of long hair, which becomes felt upon them like a garment during the inclement season. Their colour is generally bay or brown, sometimes mixed with white, and often it is of a dullish black, and sometimes piebald. They are sagacious and cunning, stealing into the patches of growing corn when opportunity offers. They are gentle, and easily reduced to obedience, and when domesticated and kindly treated, exhibit almost as much sagacity as a dog. They will enter an apartment and receive crumbs from the table, and stretch themselves on the floor. They have sometimes been put in hampers, and thus carried to a distance. They are in great request for equestrian exhibitions, and are more easily trained to the feats required than any other kind of horses.

The following is a standard description of the modern Shetlander:

Height of registered stock must not exceed ten hands at three years old and 10.5 hands at four years old and over. Colour: black is the foundation colour, but can be bay, brown, chstnut, grey, piebald, skewbald, etc. The coat changes in texture according to the seasons of the year—double coat in winter and smooth in summer. The head is well-shaped and the ears are nicely placed; it is broad in forehead, with a fairly straight face. The neck should rise off an oblique shoulder; it should be strong and muscular, with good crest, especially in stallions. The body should be thick set and deep ribbed, with a short back, broad chest and quarter. The tail should be well set on. Loins: strong and muscular. Legs: forelegs well placed under the shoulder and chest. Hind legs: thighs strong and muscular with broad, sharply developed hocks. Feet: tough and round. There should be a profuse mane and tail, and feathering of straight hair. Action: straight full movement, fore and aft, bending knees and hocks well.

In other words this is a well-built, cold-blooded horse, one metre in height, and of any equine colour.

Shetland ponies were being introduced to underground mining in large numbers about the time Queen Victoria ascended the throne. The powerful little horses proved highly successful in giving muscle to the labour of removing coal from its dismal, dark and distant subterranean sources across the central belt of Scotland, the north-east of England, and South Wales. The need of industry above ground was greater and greater coal supply. The production of coal was essential to the fuel-hungry operations of the industrial revolution which had taken place throughout Britain, not least in the Scottish Lowland Belt. Ponies worked wonders down the mines. The pit pony was a decisive factor in the wealth of Britain before World War II. The heavy industries were built upon, coal, and the pony was responsible for making it flow freely.

The extent to which the coal mines depended on pony power is

151

Shetland ponies in their social roles (around 1905). Top and bottom L—traditional work in the Shetlands; bottom R—a fancy use on the mainland

indicated by the official number of ponies in the mines in Britain prior to World War I which was given as 73,026 of which the majority were Shetlanders. The ponies used in coal mining probably numbered close

152

to a million in the course of the 130 years they were employed down the mines. Some collieries had a turnover of five or six ponies a week to replace injured or killed animals in their ruthless exploitation as cheap labour. By the end of World War II the pit pony census in Britain was down to 20,880 and dropping, as the pony era came to a timely end. Ponies were given periodical veterinary inspections and tests for glanders—a serious disease transmissible from horse to man—before its eradication. But accidents were so commonplace that these veterinary visits barely touched the problem. Treatment was certainly provided, more expeditiously, to ponies injured or sick and brought to the surface. Then they were given the run of the fields around the pit head. But many injuries below ground were so severe that humane slaughter was more common than veterinary medicine.

What never ceased to amaze those who encountered pit ponies was the absolute trust that they showed towards people. They also showed a remarkable willingness to be friends, and there was no doubt that they showed real intelligence. This may have been partly due to their native qualities but it was almost certainly enhanced by the intensive experiences they had down the pits, working closely with men and boys. The pony was usually five years of age before it was given underground work, and by the age of ten many of them had matured to the point of having such remarkable intelligence that many people were convinced that they were possessed of extrasensory perception. For example, it was often noticed that ponies were sensitive to shifts in the overhead ceilings of the underground roads before these events were known to the men working in the underground seam. In a number of cases the reaction of ponies to imminent falls of stone and earth saved numerous men from being injured, killed or trapped down the mines. Certainly the men and boys who worked with these ponies were in many cases convinced that the intelligence of the animal was equal to their own, at least in regard to the things which mattered most at work.

The size of the ponies chosen for the mines was determined to a large extent by the height of the tunnels. Some pits which had thick coal seams and high tunnels were able to use full-sized horses, but these were comparatively few. In the main, the work called for strong, sturdy ponies under fourteen hands in height. Ponies meeting these physical requirements were drawn into the pits of various parts of Britain. Small Welsh ponies were used in some mines but Shetland ponies were used most extensively. Other ponies from the New

Forest, Dartmoor, Exmoor and the Dales were pressed into mine work in substantial numbers.

The sturdy little horses were usually given the task of pulling about a ton of coal in a trolley along small railway tracks leading from a point near the coalface to a higher level in the mine workings, where the coal could then be conveyed to the pit shaft by mechanical means. There is no doubt that in many instances the workload given to the pony was far in access of what was allowed by regulations. It was virtually impossible to have regulations concerning pony welfare implemented deep in the bowels of the earth. Many ponies which learned the tricks of the trade were able to keep working down the pits well into their teens although many were retired at ten years of age.

When they were not working in the tunnels, the ponies were kept in stables down the pits. The stables were usually a long passage about fifteen feet wide with one side divided off by wooden partitions into stalls, access to which was from the paved walk behind them. The roofs of these stables were supported by girders on huge props and heavy planks of wood stretched from girder to girder to provide protection against stone falls. Ventilation in the stables was a problem, as also was the infestation of mice and rats and flies. With the best will in the world pony keepers in the mines had an impossible job to provide a high degree of welfare for these animals when they were not working and being kept in the stable. Nevertheless the little ponies were tough enough to withstand the rigours of work and it was believed that a pit pony, pound for pound, could do more work in a day than a farm horse could do in a week. It is possible that this claim would be justified in many cases.

One of the basic features of pony sensory ability was its proficiency in negotiating the underground roads of the mines in total darkness. In the main part of the mine the principal haulage roads would be quite wide, perhaps sixteen feet, and two sets of rails would be laid along these roads for ingoing and outcoming traffic of coal tubs. Full tubs were hauled from the face and empty tubs returned. These main haulage roads sometimes extended for more than a mile from the pit shaft to the coal face. Throughout their length they were girded with thick wooden props. Closer to the coal face the roads became narrower and lower and, at this point, very little light from miners' lamps penetrated the intense darkness. The darkness down a mine is totally different to darkness as it is understood on the surface. Even in the darkness of night above ground there is usually some small quantity of light being reflected from the moon, either directly or indirectly; but in the interior of the mine, darkness is complete. Whereas one's eyes can become accustomed to the darkness at ground level, this is not possible with impenetrable darkness under-ground. Down the pit, without a lamp, there was no light whatever. The darkness was oppressive as a solid black.

In spite of this pitch dark, the ponies regularly found their way from road to road and would walk perhaps a mile or more to the pit bottom from their stable. During these journeys in total darkness they hardly ever bumped into any obstacle, and this led to a firm belief among those who worked with them that they were possessed of a sixth sense to guide them with unerring accuracy through the underground workings. Memory, of course, played a part in the animal's ability to negotiate roadways by itself. It was typical of the pit pony that, despite its weight, possibly three to four hundred kilos, it was possessed of a lightness of gait. When it exercised its tremendous power it did so with the free movement of an athlete.

Pit ponies were not without their vices. One of their habits down the mines was to chew the bark off pit props when they were able to get at them. Perhaps this was not so much of a vice as a desire to vary an otherwise monotonous diet. The idiosyncracies of the animals were based upon their own particular temperament, and any other vices or characteristics which they had acquired made up the total personality of each animal. Those who worked efficiently with these animals did so by adapting themselves to the pony and not forcing it to adapt to their wishes. But in spite of this there were too many miners who thought the pit pony was there to be used, exploited—even abused—instead of being appreciated. Ponies sweated profusely. The entire surface of the skin would glisten with the saturation of sweat. The removal of this sweat became difficult in the underground conditions and many of these animals, in spite of cleaning periodically, had an unpleasant rancid odour from the dried-out sweat in their coats.

Sometimes hatred would develop between ponies, and when given their freedom they would attack each other with astonishing determi-nation, showing that this was no mock battle between animals to assert dominance; nor was this like some ritual contest between males for possession of a harem of mares. This was a clear example of the use of aggressive behaviour between animals for the evident purpose of inflicting as much injury on the other as possible. But some very intimate types of affiliation between ponies were seen in the

155

The Scots Greys on active service. Top left—in the Boer War. Others—charging at Waterloo (1815)

mines. Occasionally a very close friendship would be formed between two ponies and, when opportunity permitted, these ponies would sometimes engage in homosexual activities with each other. Miners did not usually encourage this type of thing in their ponies; but there was little doubt, in life underground, there was much that was unnatural and stressful so that peculiarities in behaviour were inevitable.

When the ponies were taken above ground for two weeks' summer break in work, they would usually give vigorous shows of freedom. Some of the ponies would frisk and dart about the fields in complete abandon—like lambs playing; some even went into a frenzy of liberated behaviour. The sheer exuberance of the ponies when taken above ground and allowed to breathe fresh air, see the green grass around, feel the warmth of the sun and smell the open environment was an amazing sight. A pit pony brought above ground became a changed animal. The older ponies in particular, who had experienced this moment before, would gallop, kick, leap and charge in sheer enjoyment. They would speed in one direction to halt sharply, then prance, then race off in another direction. The ponies expressed friendly feelings to their handlers and to one another by rumblings in their throats. This rumbling, perhaps akin to purring in cats, would be particularly evident in these playful situations.

Complaints of misuse of ponies reached the authorities as the years went by. The chief cause of these was described as lack of understanding between pony and driver, but his was far from the truth. The main source of the trouble was in the ruthless exploitation that forced the pony drivers to get the maximum work out of their horses. The authorities were not without blame here. Very few of the young drivers of these ponies were given satisfactory training before they engaged in this work.

In the main, geldings were used down mines. Mares, because of the likelihood of their going into a breeding state periodically, were considered unsuitable for pit conditions. On a few occasions some male horses were left entire and these little stallions were thought to have greater strength and vigour and to be capable of greater work than their gelded brothers. Some of these males could be demons for work and demons by nature, too. A few pits favoured stallions but the majority used only geldings. Whereas some horses and ponies were unfit to work after ten years of age, others found themselves able to adapt to the stresses and strains of pit life, and in many cases twenty years of age was reached by ponies before retiring. Contrary to general belief, the pit pony did not go blind after entering the mines. Nor did he go blind when removed from the depths of mines to the fields for the two weeks of summer each year when he was allowed a holiday. The pony's vision was no different to that of the miner in that regard.

It is possible that the last of the Galloway breed, around the Solway Firth, were lost in service down the mines. For example, a full description is given of one Galloway-type gelding whose source was given as 'unknown' to the pit authorities. He was described as being '14 hands high and seemed to be built of solid muscle'. He was as 'black as the night itself and extremely broad and deep in the chest'. It would appear distinctly possible that the Galloway ponies from the south-west of Scotland came to an end as the result of being utilized in mining.

Pit ponies were subject to variations in mood, perhaps like anyone in regular employment. In some of these moods the ponies vented their feelings and energies in work. On some of these occasions they would attack their work with such vigour that all who saw such a performance were impressed. One such demonstration is described by a miner and writer, Eric Squires, as follows:

> What a sight! Such strength in that beautiful body and such coordination of its power! He would haul that run of tubs up the slope until the sheer weight forced him to slow, pace by pace and finally he was brought to a leg-trembling halt. Back he would go, little by little, until he decided to go forward again, launching himself into the collar with new and devastating strength; and this was where his belly would actually rub against the sleepers.

Miners were convinced that the pit pony was possessed of occult sense and that he made intelligent use of this by associating situations with accidents that had happened down the pits. This sense of awareness increased with experience, and although it was not particularly well developed in young ponies of five or six years, it was very well-developed by the time the pony was ten years of age.

In the stable these little horses required to be approached with a great deal of caution for many of them were given to vicious kicking at anyone approaching them from the rear when they were in their stables. Their hooves could slice through the air in a flash and often did so, injuring people coming behind them unaware of the danger. Working in the stall with them was sometimes quite hazardous because they had further vices—snapping with their teeth, biting viciously and some of them slicing with side kicks, or 'mule kicks', at anyone in the stall with them. But they could be sensitive creatures too, and when pony drivers took the trouble to make friends with them they would almost invariably respond with affectionate attachment. The extreme viciousness of some pit ponies was not typical. Many of them, in fact, would have made excellent riding ponies for children if they had not, by fate, been pressed into service down the mine. On retirement, a few did become pets. Some of those mining ponies were so much more suitable for a role above ground that it was an utter injustice that they were committed to mining for most or all of their adult lives.

Before being sent down the pits to begin their life's work there, ponies about five years of age were usually given a short period of training. An attempt was made to simulate the conditions of the pit, so that many of the working requirements there could be practised above ground. But there were some subterranean features that could not be reproduced, and these were among those which seemed to cause most distress to some ponies. First of all there was the initial introduction. As the pony was walked on the cage at the pit head and the gate closed behind him he was then left alone, for no miner was allowed to travel down with the animal in the cage for reasons of safety. The cage would move slowly downwards until the landing had been cleared. After that point down the shaft it literally dropped. The speed of the drop was usually in the order of 30 miles per hour. At the end of the descent new ponies were usually led off the cage in a state of terror. It was little wonder that they were found difficult to handle from the very beginning of their underground careers. The noise echoing from the empty tubs with which they worked was also a source of terror. Their surroundings were stressful and undoubtedly led to a higher incidence of vice in these animals than would have been developed by them in more natural working conditions. They were a cheap form of labour, however, and very little regard was given to the refinements of their welfare. This was not the only type of horse taken for granted in our history. We lost the Galloway breed, from oversight.

The Galloway Nag was a medium-sized horse of great versatility which was in wide use in Britain from the time of Shakespeare to Walter Scott, both having referred to the horse in their works. No modern description of this horse can be found since it apparently became extinct as a breed in the second half of the nineteenth century. It originated in the broad region of Galloway, and its general dispersal to other parts of the country took place through Dumfries. Due to its great usefulness in riding, in carriage work and in light draft work, it was in great demand and was widely recognised as a horse of quality. Unique were the qualities of this horse which was 14 hands (142 cms) in height, dark in colour (certainly dark limbs), and with endurance, and vigour in its gait. A full account of this horse was given by Professor Low in 1845 as follows:

> A variety of horses, differing from the ordinary pack-horses in their greater lightness and elegance of figure, were termed Galloways. They exceeded the pony size, and were greatly valued for their activity and bottom. They were derived from the counties near the Solway Firth; and an opinion frequently expressed is, that they had been early improved by horses saved from the wreck of the Armada. There is nothing beyond tradition to support this opinion, and it is known that the Horses of Galloway were distinguished long before the age of the Armada. The nature of the country, mountainous, but not heathy and barren, may account for the production of a larger race of ponies, without resorting to the supposition of foreign descent.

Peacetime activities of the Lovat Scouts (above) and Scots Greys (below). Both around 1908

Besides, this part of Scotland was a country of forays during the rude border wars of the times, when a more agile race than the ordinary pack-horse was naturally sought for; and all along the borders of the two kingdoms, a class of similar properties existed. Many of the true Galloways of the western counties

160

were handsome, and their general characteristic was activity, and the power of enduring fatigue. In former times this breed was in great demand in England, and the people of Galloway where they were produced, up to a period not very distant, were noted as horse-dealers.

In fact, horse breeders throughout Galloway produced large numbers for use in England. It was Scotland's principal export commodity in its day. Many were supplied to King Edward I for court and country service. Conceivably this horse was the start of Scotland's export trading. It certainly became a well-established animal throughout England.

The outstanding horse authority in Britain in the nineteenth century was William Youatt, who considered the Galloway superior to all other ponies native to the British Isles. In 1858 he gave his account of the animal, indicating its point of extinction:

> A horse between thirteen and fourteen hands in height is called a *Galloway*, from a beautiful breed of little horses once found in the south of Scotland, on the shore of the Solway Firth, but now sadly degenerated, and almost lost.
>
> The pure Galloway was said to be nearly fourteen hands high, and sometimes more; of a bright bay, or brown, with black legs, small head and neck, and peculiarly deep and clean legs. Its qualities were speed, stoutness, and surefootedness over a very rugged and mountainous country.
>
> Some remains of the old Galloways are still to be met with in the Isle of Mull; but they are altogether neglected, and fast degenerating from admixture with inferior breeds.

In its heyday the Galloway was noted for its endurance in riding. In 1754 one of the breed was put to a marathon test over the Newmarket course where it 'went one hundred miles a day, for three successive days, without the slightest distress'. (It would be a good second-hand car which could do that today.) A Dr. Anderson described his eighteenth-century Galloway and its performance as follows:

> In point of elegance of shape, it was a perfect picture; and in disposition was gentle and compliant. It moved almost with a wish, and never tired. I rode this little creature for twenty-five years, and twice in that time I rode a hundred and fifty miles at a stretch, without stopping except to bait, and that not for above an hour at a time. It came in at the last stage with as much ease and alacrity as it travelled the first. I could have undertaken to have performed on this beast, when it was in its prime, sixty miles a day for a twelvemonth, running without any extraordinary exertion.

In addition to its wide use in England, the Galloway was also exported to British colonies, including Newfoundland, the oldest colony. In the eighteenth century, ponies were needed in many Newfoundland outports to haul up fishing boats, cart logs, pull traps and maintain overland communication throughout this large island. A light versatile animal was needed, and those of Galloway type filled the bill. Many of these horses were procured from English regions, and inferior pony types indigenous to locations close to ports of embarkation, such as Bristol, undoubtedly went with them to the New World—Newfoundland and New England. All this was, of course, before there was any pony breed society to define standards, register animals and their breeding, and otherwise organise the affairs of regionalized stock. In the absence of responsible patronage the Galloway's over-exploitation resulted in its demise. Its source was not being protected and preserved, as farmers in Galloway became more concerned with the breeding of large agricultural horses. In the development of the extensive arable land of Galloway lay much potential wealth. A cash trade in ponies was no match for the emergent agricultural revolution which was taking place in the shadows of the industrial revolution in Scotland and elsewhere. That the Galloway Nag is is now extinct is essentially true, although some Galloway types—which have been free each summer for over two hundred years to breed naturally—still exist in Newfoundland. Embraced by the general breed-type unofficially called 'The Newfoundland Pony', larger specimens of this type remain as Galloway descendants which still serve their communities by pulling logs from the timber woods for winter fuel in the outport houses of people who can easily trace their roots directly back to Britain and Ireland. Although they have not been documented, the mixed roots of their ponies are no less direct and undoubtedly extend to the Galloway source, to some degree.

The Lovat Scouts were a military force of mounted volunteers raised chiefly in the Highlands. The detachment which left for the Boer War at the end of the nineteenth century took a large number of excellent mounts. Although they were mostly Highland ponies, they had been carefully selected for maximum size and were over 14.2 hands (144 cms) in height, the recognised limit for pony classification. The distinguished service of this force and its mounts reflected credit on the home breed, of which they were legitimate members. Highland pony blood, to some degree, went into military service.

The mainland ponies, especially those grey in colour, found increasing favour in the south of Scotland in the 1700s. They crossed nicely with the draught horses of the arable farms there. Their crosses made good dual-purpose animals, for riding and for seasonal work. The moss-troopers of the Scottish Borders used such grey horses exclusively. In the south-west similar 'Bonnie Greys', or dapple greys, were also bred from Highlanders. They featured in Ayrshire, where the famous grey mare Meg, described by Burns in 'Tam o'Shanter', was representative of such a type—'a finer never lifted leg'. It was a similar grey which Burns' Old Farmer saluted on a 'New Year's Morning'. Such greys set a model for military horses in the south-east of Scotland, later to become the standard mounts of Scotland's premier cavalry regiment—The Greys.

11 Horse Sense

The age of the working horse gave the public a kinship with animals. Among Nature's living beings, the horse, in so many ways, offered a model to live by. The horse had an air of dignity as he moved with precision, authority and restrained strength. The great power was preserved for instances of personal effort. The horse affiliated, fraternised and made loyal bonds readily with the people who used him. Touches of delicacy were constantly displayed by the horse in the way he ate, stepped, and responded in his choice of action. In his habits he was circumspect. A creature of great contrasts, no other could be so bold and so cautious, so independent and so cooperative, so primitive and so refined, so durable and so vulnerable, so elemental and yet complex.

If man has a soul, the horse has some equivalent state of deep, inner being. A horse is living sculpture, symmetrical beauty, solid mass, fine construction, all with artistic trimmings. Through rich shades of matt colour, the shadowed sparkling eyes and the rippling body comes the essence of equine presence. It may be the most finely finished living product of nature and antiquity. When the horse was mankind's chief companion, how much quality it surely gave to life, how much pure service too. As a model, it was really a difficult challenge for man to copy, but it could still be respected, even loved, and as a rule it was, by the men who worked with it.

When horses provided all the power for field work, every farmer was a horseman—and usually an expert one. In much the same way as mothers intuitively understand their small children, so horsemen could, without the use of any recognisable communication, comprehend fully the wants, the fears, the moods, the discomforts, the pains, the satisfactions and the peculiar personal idiosyncrasies of their animals. They could not live closely with their horses and work with them in all weathers and circumstances without developing a keen understanding of them. The horse is by no means a dumb creature, and many of its vocalizations are understandable to those who have come to learn their significance; it is in body language, or behaviour, that the horse tells of its moods and mental states.

In the equine age no man ever pleaded horse ignorance. Everyone was believed—with much justification—to know horses. Any show of ignorance of horses would have been an acute embarrassment, on a par with illiteracy today. Much understanding seemed like a two-way form of extra-sensory perception, ingrained with mutual experience. The measure of a farm worker was often his 'horse sense'—hence that expression. It was no small subject either; this workers' 'horseology'; it encompassed breeding, selecting, aging, breaking, harnessing; special topics included conformation, anatomical terms, habits, needs, diseases, signs of illness, home treatments, vices and temperaments and general care. Technical equine discussions never ceased. They invaded gossip and chat in the farm kitchen, made up most of the stable talk and filled most gaps in conversation whenever farming people met and wherever horsemen gathered.

The extent to which horses commanded attention was not surprising. Virtually all the working day was occupied with the management of horses. All boys, either in country or town, grew up in a world full of horses—on fields, roads and streets.

On the farm, horses were workers, helpers and partners in muck-spreading, ploughing, harrowing, discing, drilling and rolling the soil. At harvest they pulled the various items of machinery such as cutter, reaper, binder, hay rake, hay bogie and corn cart. Even when the horse's work was ended for the day, the horseman was still there, drying, wiping, grooming, watering, feeding and bedding for an extra hour in the partnership. At springtime, the horseman would often be midwife and nurse when a foal was born. When the horses were out at grass the good horseman made brief visits to his animals in the evening or weekend, to ensure that all was well; for the equine contract was based on sympathy. The close relationship between horse and farm worker made many a country wife a weary horse-widow.

Much earnest endeavour was in each horse's fibre, shown in the way he would proudly nod his head strongly in rhythm with each plodding effort. None could plod like the Clydesdale. With every flourished tread of the great hooves—the largest in the entire equine world—this horse would gain a commanding foothold on his share of the world. Uphill or in heavy going, the animal might snort with each strenuous step, emphasizing effort. In the taciturn carter a love would grow, year by year, for these boldly-marked, powerful, hard-working animals.

The working bond between ploughman and horse meant more than the endless toil of cultivation; it could supply a deep appreciation of natural life. To a man who, apart from the soil and his family, had very little of material satisfaction, farming by horse meant much. It was, after all, the chosen way of life. The debt to the working horse was not small, nor was it ignored by the farming generations.

In their own ways the working horses reacted mainly to the regular activities around them. As the horses heard the approach of the horseman starting the day's work, they would whinny out the calls for attention, for watering and feeding. In a big stable, their chorus made a demanding noise which hurried the horseman to lead them out, two at a time, to the watering trough in the yard. To the horses in their stalls wooden buckets, spilling with water, were carried in haste. Immediately after watering, sweet hay would be thrown into the mangers of the hungry horses. Some would not be satisfied with this offering and would continue their whinnies, bang the manger and paw at the floor, demanding their corn ration which came last, like dessert. Horses are low on patience where food is concerned.

Other reactions of horses in tense situations could be less predictable, and less amusing. When presented with a challenging situation a horse can only do one of three things: the thing it has been trained to do, an attempt at flight, or a fighting response. Working with horses was never the safest occupation because of their occasional unpredictable reactions. An upset horse could kick with sledgehammer force. He could sometimes place a great, heavy foot carelessly on a horseman's boot. Making a cripple out of a horseman was seldom the result of a horse's maliciousness, more often it was the outcome of a startled reaction in a confused, alarmed or irritated animal. A giant, programmed by instinct to react quickly and reflexively ahead of his own thinking, can hurt even a friend in automatic self-defence.

Most feared of all equine misadventures was the runaway. With an individual horse or team, bolting was often the cause of accidents to man and beast alike. Bolting could happen anywhere—often on a road, sometimes in a field. A horse would bolt, or 'spook', when he suddenly caught sight of something extraordinary closing in on his presence. The sudden flight of a bird or leap of a rabbit, paper being swept in the wind, clothing or sheeting flapping in the breeze, all could fill the inexperienced—or unhappily experienced—horse with a wild urge to take flight. Few horse people had not some first-hand knowledge of a traumatic runaway episode. The runaway team could cause the destruction of equipment and of horses on a drastic scale. In a large team, the 'runaway fever' seemed to affect quickly the entire gang after one of its members was suddenly inclined to bolt in fear. Bolting was an infectious reaction dreaded by horsemen and beyond their control. It was beyond the control of horses themselves, and bolters were sometimes injured so severely that their humane destruction was necessary.

Horses stabled alone for any reason reacted badly to their imprisonment. Working horses, so accustomed to daily excursions with outlets for their need of action, took isolated enclosure badly. It was a horseman's saying that 'any horse kept on its own is in damned bad company'. The bored horse in the stable would be likely to acquire some stable vice such as biting on the manger ('cribbing') and 'windsucking'. These vices tended to become ingrained habits after their initial occurrence. A common stable vice was 'weaving'—walking on the spot with the forelegs, while swaying the head from side to side rhythmically in animated weariness.

All vices partly reduced the animal's fitness, usefulness and value. Working horses saw a lot of stables and they were thus prone to pernicious habits arising from constrained idleness or illness. Exercise and work were as one, to all appearances; both fully occupied the animal and seemed to be taken for horse-games by the fitter animals. Stall-kicking was a habit induced by lack of work or exercise arising from long-term, stall enclosure. Stall-kicking horses would kick forcefully with their hind feet at the rear posts of their stall partitions. It was a villainous practice which destroyed the boarding of stable walls and stall partitions. Destruction of property, whether by man or beast, was much frowned upon in those hard times.

Although working horses did not like to be restrained alone in empty stables, they were apparently glad enough of them as home. Once turned on the homeward-bound leg of a journey, they would perk up, improving their stride, lifting their heads and putting more weight into the collar, although they would doubtless be more tired then than when they left their stall-beds. Horses have strong homing instincts which seem to operate on a 'mental compass', gyroscopically working continuously as they are driven along complex changes of direction. The horse's affinity for his home base is keen and knowledge of its general direction is good. Left to his own devices by a drowsing driver, an experienced cart horse could travel the road home in safety. He could even find his way back to a stable in town, without mishap, in those halcyon days before automobile traffic. Nothing, it seemed, so pleased a horse as the chance to go directly to his stable where there would be unharnessing, food, water, and bedding in a familiar environment: home in fact. To meet its fundamental needs, the working horse knew of nowhere but the stable. When these needs became keen, at the end of a hard day of leg-work, his homing drive was sharp indeed. It seemed that a stable home was wonderful to leave and equally wonderful to return to.

Horses reacted strongly to other horses. Their 'conversations' used a body language of subtle signals, feints, expressions, nips and postures. A mild nip with the bared incisor teeth on the shoulder of an associate would affirm an alliance, albeit one of unequal rank. Acceptance of this message in such a gesture might be shown by the other horses in a subdued squeal, with raised head and flattened ears. Showing the white of the eye to another horse spoke of a readiness to defend position. Whinnying variously expressed determination or frustration in the current situation. But vocal language was less in use than visual communication in which simple signals were used. The wide eye warned and the flaring nostrils told a tale of adrenalin flowing; eyes rolled when a hostile attitude developed. A relaxed facial expression, with the ears outward and the eye lids relaxed, gave the lie to a phoney open-mouthed threat, for it merely indicated its playful purpose. When the face was set with muscles contracted, the eye protruding and ears twisted back, real anger was being expressed and the intent of an aggressive act, such as a vicious bite or kick, was being announced. Swinging the hindquarters at another was the unkindest show of all. A 'two-barrelled' kick was often the next statement in such expressions of dislike.

A work-horse left for a time, standing in harness in the field or street, was normally inclined to dose off in a light sleep, the head bobbing occasionally. The fore limbs would be close together and held well under the chest while the hind feet were usually placed with one slightly ahead of the other under the belly. The advanced hind limb would sometimes knuckle over in a flexed state of relaxation. This was the 'stand-easy' posture and its strategic use would allow the horse to gain about a total hour of drowsing in the working day—when the work breaks permitted. Drowsing in the same manner was also practised in several short spells in the quietness of the stable at night, for a total of about one and a half hours. Some true sleeping (of the 'slow brain-wave' type) could also be done standing, promoting the general belief that horses slept standing up. This is a half-truth for, although they can have some 'slow wave sleep' while standing, they prefer to lie down for this. The other form of true body sleep (with rapid eye movements) was only really possible when the horse lay down flat on his side. This required the privacy and space of the bedded stall. No regular patterns of sleeping are clearly shown by all horses, for there is random dispersal of short sleep periods each night, amounting to about three hours in total. Nocturnal sleep periods are typically short and irregularly spaced with wakeful rest. This is one of the horse's principal mechanisms for self-protection. It is an inheritance of bygone millenia—a primitive sleeping style of a prehistoric age.

In the era of the horse there was much life in the raw. The procreative and physical mainstays of life were dominant facts— particularly in the rural communities. Country life at its vibrant best contained the most natural features of living. Big horses acted out their sex roles in the grand manner. The horseman was usually the first to know of the mare in her breeding state in the late springtime. Subtle change in disposition was the first sign in the mare which told the horseman that equine fancy was stirring. The little harnessing rituals were borne less patiently by the mare as her breeding time (or estrus) developed quickly. The collar would not be allowed to go over her head so easily; bridling was subtly resisted. Horsemen did not like their working mares in heat since the horse was then an additional nuisance. At work between the shafts of the cart, the mare's occasional stop to urinate now became a nuisance.

Breeding behaviour in mares shows a range of characteristics peculiar to this species. The intensity of their sexual drive varies probably more than in any of the other farm species. A mare in estrus (or heat) typically assumes frequent, straddled stances. During these, mucoid urine is ejected in small quantities which may splash at the animal's heels. Following this, the animals maintain the straddling stance for a time with the hind limbs held apart and extended. The tail is lifted so as to be arched away from the vulva. The heels of one or other hind hoof were usually tilted up so that only the toe of that hoof remained touching the ground. While this stance was maintained, the animal showed flashing of the clitoris by repeated rhythmic contractions of the vulva. The duration of equine estrus was four to six days on average but varied; some lasted only one day and others up to twenty.

When big horses copulated there were a lot of large moving parts. Hooves swung, there was rearing, mounting and remounting. Grooms facilitating the natural process had a hazardous job. The stallion was led up to the mare by the bridle and allowed to mount. The man in charge of the stallion stood well forward alongside the mare when the horse mounted. Sometimes the groom had to guide the horse's penis by hand, while others held the mare by her halter and the stallion by a bridle for extra control. Most stallions attempted to mount on two or more occasions before making a deliberate attempt to serve. Rushing movements, or any display likely to frighten the mare, were discouraged. If the stallion showed any inclination to bite the mare's neck during the act of service, precautions were taken to prevent this habit developing. A leather muzzle was sometimes applied for this. Every effort was made to avoid mares being startled at the critical moments. With the business of procreation aside, there was every likelihood of being pregnant and of producing her equine infant about eleven months later on some quiet night.

Early experiences permanently affected the behaviour of a horse in adult life. Events and experiences in early life have a more powerful and durable influence than those in later life. The immature horse is more impressionable than the adult, and alarming experiences, in particular, tend to have more effect the earlier in life they are experienced. The horse benefits from as much variety of experience as possible in the early developmental age. Between birth and weaning, the total effects of learning are consolidated. The development of emotions, the opportunity to pursue exploratory behaviour, the social experience of the young foal, and the development of its physical and physiological apparatus, all combine to influence subsequent behaviour and character. Post-weaning experiences also play their part in developing later behaviour. Learning continues throughout life; the senses also continue to develop and improve the horse's awareness of its whole environment.

A major means of learning is trial and error. Such learning occurs from numerous exploratory activities in the course of self-development. Many horses are behaviourally 'shaped' by being rewarded for fairly desirable actions. The horse may be further rewarded for correct response to a command. The command is likely to be associated with some 'aid' to encourage action. Eventually, the trained horse can be induced to perform complicated and relatively unnatural tasks on command.

Learning occurs very quickly and easily during 'sensitive periods'. A sensitive period is a time in an animal's life during which it is open to influence. Some 'sensitive periods' coincide with acute operation of the senses when the animal is particularly susceptible to fast learning. The horse acquires durable impressions during these periods of phenomenal awareness. Animals in such periods may be at a given stage of nervous development—key biological points, such as early life, weaning and puberty.

Learning forms memory and this appears to take place through an initial formation of a short-term memory and the subsequent formation of a long-term memory 'trace'. The latter consolidates what has been learned. The formation of long-term memory traces appear to occur more readily in the horse than most other animals. The two stages of learning formation are readily discernible in horses, and give them phenomenal memory formation. Older memory traces are evidently the most consolidated and are resistant to removal, being deeply ingrained. Undoubtedly the horse has a great capacity for retaining past experience. Memories of pain and fear are the most persistent, long after the unpleasant event has passed. Memories of such episodes are virtually impossible to eradicate in a horse. Its behaviour, it seems, may continue to be affected by the memories of certain painful situations. If a horse is hurt or is punished for doing something which is natural to it, it will be very difficult to eradicate this fear at any later date in spite of continuous rewards given when it performs properly.

In horse breaking, behaviour is shaped by rewarding the action and subsequently presenting the reward only on the performance of that action. In this respect animal training resembles drilling. Repetition is important, as is consistency. In such training a start is made by rewarding, through encouragement, any successful act which approximates the behaviour which is desired. The old, experienced trainers tried firstly to get a horse to do something similar to the desired action. Thereafter they increasingly rewarded only those behaviours which were close to the purpose of the training. The skill of the trainer lay in recognizing small progressive responses and rewarding each of these. Even the smallest progress in training could be the key to the desired performance. As training neared completion the desired responses alone would be reinforced by reward. Verbal praise and appreciative patting served as adequate rewards for desired behaviours.

The men with keenest horse sense knew that in training which involved an elimination of some undesired behaviour such as biting, the punishment must be made to coincide with the misbehaviour. For instance, horses could be trained to stop biting by being pricked with a sharp nail or pin in the upper lip at the moment of an attempted bite. In the main, however, experience showed that punishment was not a particularly successful method of horse training.

The wise old equine experts came to the conclusion that, in the synchronized relationships between horse and horseman, there was no need for crude mechanisms such as a fierce bit to control a normal horse. The best trainers worked with the horse's natural reactions, supplementing and moulding their inborn responses with carefully chosen learned habits. This produced a well-trained and well-integrated animal capable of producing responses markedly different, eventually, from its natural, untrained activities.

Forms of intelligent behaviour could be observed in working horses. Impressive displays of intellectual properties were often witnessed, for example in the ways horses could anticipate what was next wanted of them. While various methods are often used to attempt to measure intelligence in animals, it is now supposed, in animal science, that the length of time that an animal can remember specific training can be taken as some measure of intelligence. Promptness in learning is also evidence of intelligence, and many examples of this can be seen in horses.

A horse's reactions, which collectively make up its characteristic behaviour, are often determined by its temperament. The way that a horse uses senses such as vision, hearing and smell is also affected by his own temperament. Movements of eyelids and the eyeball are important indicators; the upper eyelids contract when he is emotionally aroused. Excessive mobility of the eyeball in the stationary horse was an indication of anxiety, recognised by the knowledgeable horseman. On the other hand a very glazed, fixed state of the eye indicated distress, such as from pain.

Most aggressive reactions in horses are shown when they are in their own company. Much of the restless activities are to determine the status of each horse in the group. In a typical encounter between two horses of different social status in the one group, one horse will act aggressively, reaching out to snap at the skin around the shoulders and neck of the adversary. If the adversary then recognizes that it is subordinate in the social hierarchy to the animal attacking it, its response will be one of quick submission or avoidance. At this point the aggressive exchange between the two animals ceases since its purpose has been fulfilled. Minor aggressive acts are shown when one horse's 'individual space' has been violated by the sudden intrusion of another horse.

Many reactions among horses take the form of vocal expressions. Among horse calls are three basic ones, namely, a neigh, a grunt and a high-pitched whinny. These sounds vary in the degree of intensity and duration; minor variations occur according to the sex and age of the horse and to the particular type of stimulus which has caused the vocal expression. The neigh and whinny are the long-distance calls. They are often given when a horse is curious or concerned about events happening beyond its range of vision. Grunting and threat noises are various; the most frequent one is that type expressed at feeding time when a mixture of hunger and excitement seem to be the stimulating forces for this vocal expression. The neighing sound varies in volume from one set of circumstances to another, such as when the horse is seeking to communicate with others some distance away. Squealing is often heard during short, sharp encounters between horses, or when one horse attacks another unexpectedly.

Additional forms of vocal expression in horses include the trumpeting neigh of the stallion in a state of sexual arousal. Gurgling throaty sounds are common in both sexes of all ages and are produced in circumstances which indicate that the horse is expressing general satisfaction, for example when it had been fully fed or when it greets approvingly the arrival of a human or another horse. One interesting sound used by horses is the wicker. A low wicker is frequently used as a message of welcome or an invitation to 'come here'. By raising the note of the wicker the horse can make the communication more emphatic. This welcoming call has several different tones which vary the intensity of the greeting call. Each horse has its own individual 'language', using sounds to convey various meanings. Distinct notes convey a message by sounds which vary from a low snuffle to a scream of rage, fear or pain. Anyone knowing a particular horse well can begin to understand these messages.

The ingestive habits of horses are regular. The horse, if fed only in its stall, eats for about three hours each day. About fifteen minutes daily are spent drinking, the average heavy horse taking about ten or more gallons of water daily. Horses also enjoy licking salt and they can spend up to half an hour each day licking at any available salt blocks. Horses do not require this amount of salt for their systems but there seems to be a special fondness for salt, over and above some basic need for it. Although it is true that horses eat more fastidiously than any of the other farm animals, they nevertheless seem to suffer more eating problems. Wood eating is one such problem of which horses are quite frequently guilty. Other examples of depraved appetites include the eating of bedding, of dirt, sand, tail-hairs and their own feces. Some horses develop the various bad habits of swallowing air, bolting their feed and drinking water excessively. Most of these ingestive vices are potentially dangerous to the horse since they can cause serious types of colic.

Emotional tensions in horses can affect their digestion. If they are having difficulty in adapting to their circumstances or the type of work, some horses are so emotionally affected that their digestive processes become noticeably impaired. Excess of unvaried work can result in a condition called 'sourness'. The soured horse shows deterioration in temperament and digestion, passing droppings of poorly digested food and participating relectantly in the routines of work. Its dung is then evacuated much more quickly after consumption since the digestive upset causes food to pass out of the body before it is properly digested. When such a horse becomes relaxed and accepts its conditions, its digestion can return to normal.

When they are given free range, horses spend much of their time grazing, perhaps about twelve hours or more. When grazing, they space themselves out from each other; they seem to consider it important to have freedom from conflict when in the business of eating. Horses graze by cropping the grass close to the roots with the incisor teeth. While grazing they seldom take more than two mouthfuls at one spot before moving at least one step further to the next spot. In doing this they avoid the areas where equine droppings have previously been deposited. This emphasizes their fastidious nature. Horses being kept in a small paddock graze those area where no feces have been dropped, and the pasture develops into two types of area as a result. One area becomes cropped down to look like an irregular lawn in appearance. Areas where feces have been deposited and accumulated are not grazed and they continue to grow in large tufts of very rough grass. A restrictive horse pasture which has been over-grazed shows clearly demarcated areas of 'lawns' and 'roughs', evidence of serious over-use of the land.

Horses are very gregarious animals and enjoy each other's company. Small groups tend to become closely compacted and move around a grazing area together, while still maintaining a certain amount of 'personal' area around themselves. Although they are a typical herding species, horses show a marked preference for certain individuals of their own kind. Two horses encountering each other for the first time show mutual exploratory behaviour. This involves an investigation of the other's head, body and hindquarter by smelling. Bonds of friendship can become quickly formed between pairs of horses that are allowed to associate with each other outdoors. Enmities also can develop. When they form pairs with great understanding, they seem able to read each other's intentions and to function almost as one bonded unit. Pairs of horses can enjoy states of intimate understanding.

When they have the opportunity to associate with each other at pasture, mutual body care is a part of the daily activities of horses. At pasture, pairs of horses usually spend long spells in mutual grooming. This form of grooming is shown in all age groups, though the pairs formed by individuals are usually matched for age and size; mares and their foals often groom each other. In the normal grooming arrangement two horses face each other, one extends its head past the other's neck and nibbles vigorously over its back. The other horse responds in like fashion; both then vigorously nibble over their backs simultaneously. Horses also spend some time nibbling their own bodies, especially their hips and flanks. They also groom their limbs, both the forefeet and hind, in a similar manner. Occasionally horses will clean their nostrils and faces by rubbing these up and down the inside of one foreleg and then the other.

Horses at pasture groom their backs by rolling over and working the back into the ground—usually a patch of ground which is bare of grass. In this activity the ritual is quite precise. The horse lies down in the normal fashion on its side and then proceeds to kick itself over on to its back. It then rubs its back vigorously into the earth while keeping its feet up in the air. After several rubs and rolls the horse rises to its feet and vigorously shakes all of its body. Its skin ripples and dust particles are then thrown out from its coat along with skin debris.

Horses which are running outdoors for substantial periods of time develop certain territorial habits. They soon become proprietors of certain areas and they will frequently become aggressive in defence of them, fighting with one another with their own offensive and defensive methods. They bite, kick out with their hind feet and strike with their fore feet. The horse will act out its territorial defence, kicking out with the hind feet when its 'flight distance' is violated. The flight distance is that perimeter of area which the horse views as the outer limit of its personal space. Within this it will defend or take flight when en-croached upon by another socially unacceptable animal.

The thing the horse does best, the thing it has greatest need to perform, is active movement. The need for movement is essential for a horse's physical and mental wellbeing—its welfare. Horses have a very great need for action and exercise and they use territory as space in which to run. Running is usually a group activity with one of the group setting off and generating a mood in the others to follow. The fitter the horse, the greater is its urge for exercise or work, and constant activity is needed to preserve fitness. In distant history the horse was vulnerable to predators, and nature ensured that it was provided with a style of defence and survival in the ability to run and to travel great distance without rest.

Horses have an urge to move from place to place which becomes very evident when they are enclosed within a limited space. It could be argued that the great need of the horse for company of its own kind makes it the most sociable of all animals. But this behaviour pattern is also part of the horse's natural equipment for survival. Without it horses low in the pecking order—or the social structure of the group—might be deprived of nourishment by being driven away from the preferred grazing, although even horses at the bottom of a social hierarchy will retain some capacity for self-assertion. The role of social dominance in horse groups is very real. When horses have been living in a group and the group moves from place to place throughout the pasture, it is generally observed that the same horses lead the way each time while others tend to lie to the back of the group. Some horses assume full leadership and others assume roles of followership. Some horses persistently find their way into a position of leadership in a group while others seem quite ready to accept a position low in the rank order, even in a small herd. Removed from one group and placed in a fresh one, these horses usually attain for themselves a similar level in the hierarchy which they held previously.

In the hierarchy the older and larger animals are usually found to be high in rank; stallions do not necessarily dominate geldings or mares. A dominant individual horse often dictates the movement of the herd through the grazing area, serving to act as a leader in the grazing movements. Often, with very evident jealousy, a horse will break up close encounters among other horses. Such socially dominant horses are sometimes found to have much more aggressive temperaments than the others in the group. If a group of horses of mixed sex contains a number of geldings, these male castrates are very likely to separate to the edge of the group, forming a kind of bachelor club.

Before the combustion engine finally destroyed their roles, horses not only worked for their corn but fertilized it too. They rounded off their willing service to scattered Scottish society by knitting it together with well-wheeled communication. The horse was complementary to city life, bringing to every street a rural presence. These country agents on-the-hoof were the dominant representatives of animal life to town-locked urbanity. To the carters and ploughmen of the Lowlands a cuddy was a donkey but the townies of Scotland often called their horses cuddies as a term of endearment for any donkey, horse or pony, young or old, male or female, heavy or light, pedigreed or anonymous, worker or sport. They were seen as a great equine army of workers—the pride of the nation—until after World War II and the advent of Ferguson's tractor. Petroleum power came to supplant horse power in almost every aspect of agricultural field work, and the horse and its agricultural equipment yielded to a new lifestyle dictated by consumption of oil.

As they became redundant, many horses met their end as horse flesh. Others were allowed some retirement before giving up their leather and breath to the knackerman. A few cheated him and found an end in the soil their kind had tilled and fertilized for two great centuries. As they disappeared, so did cobbled streets, smiddies, horse ferries, saddlers' shops and the men who maintained them all. Harness was burned or junked. Wheel tracks now grew grass and weeds in their middle, where horses once trod.

Horse fanciers can still find scope in showing, racing, training, jumping, eventing, as equestrian interest returns. Mounted police have proved to be the best at crowd management. Horses could be used more economically in short-distance haulage, in small crop work, and generally for mobile chores.

Horses are natural to the farm. They are the best means of carrying out sundry chores needing muscle. They are fuelled by farm crops. The horse and the farm are complementary, each benefits the other. Tillage by slow horse-drawn equipment allows aeration of soil—a valuable form of earth conditioning which reduces deterioration of land. For small to medium-sized farms especially, this and other benefits such as natural fertilization will always make horse use an attractive and economical proposition.

The imminent high cost and shortage of fuel casts doubt on the wisdom of total dependence on the fuel-hungry tractor. Some farmers are saying that the horse can be more economic power than the internal combustion engine. Studies of land use and tillage costs suggest that the horse may prove to be the best alternative source of power to oil. Ecologically too, the use of non-renewable oil does not compare favourably with the annual equine consumption of only three acres of fodder and the production of nine tons of manure.

The few farmers who persisted in using horses as a hobby—or out of seeming perversity—now use their animals as realistic sources of power and labour for many tasks on the farm. Their merits are being rediscovered—they are versatile at work, they can go over soft soil and through mud, they can work in awkward pieces of land and they can reproduce themselves profitably. At least one farmer, in the North of England, has set up a business to educate people in the agricultural uses of the horse. Others are supplying trained and harnessed horses and their equipment for field work to many young farmers who are taking the decision to farm by horse.

The farm horse's future prospects look good but the success of its return might depend on help from its early adversary, namely technology. Agricultural engineers must return to the serious study of using real horse power on the land, abandoned in the Great Depression. Modern studies are needed to determine equine efficiencies. The emergent generation of horse farmers will not surely use the old types of implements given up as cumbrous half a century ago. Modern technology could certainly improve on these and provide horse-drawn, lightweight implements of strength and reliable construction which could be operated easily with high efficiency. Accurate scientific work is still required to take horse-drawn machinery into the age of high technology. The heavy horse is no longer with us in commercially realistic numbers, and as there is a loss of livestock in quantity, there comes an inevitable loss in their quality. There is one lesson well learned from the past—horses have to be kept in our society. Potential problems of fuel availability and prices have to be looked at squarely. The outline of a backup system, for crises in cultivating market gardens, small and medium-sized farms, needs planning now. This would certainly make some provision for horse breeding.

The Clydesdale in particular, its long-term survival possibly still on a knife edge in its native country, can have its future secured with the right type of patronage. Specimens of this are numerous in Canada where quality also has been well preserved—even enhanced. Re-

179

introduction of Clydesdales from North America can revitalize the breed at home.

But there will always be a good case for horse breeding for its own special satisfaction. Horse breeding is its own reward. In natural interest, aesthetic attraction, and biological reality it is fulfilling; it keeps us in step with nature. We need to put the horse before the cart again and share that natural heritage common to ourselves and these vulnerable animals.

Index